AEROSPACE FACTS AND FIGURES

00/01

Compiled by:
Economic Data Service
Aerospace Research Center
Aerospace Industries Association of America, Inc.

Director, Research Center
David H. Napier

Editorial Consultant
Ann A. Hunter

Design
AAH Graphics, Inc.

Published by:
Aerospace Industries Association of America, Inc.
1250 Eye Street, N.W., #1200
Washington, D.C. 20005-3924
FAX (202) 371-8470

For information about orders, call (202) 371-8407
For information about content, call (202) 371-8563

ACKNOWLEDGMENTS

stacks

Air Transport Association of America

Council of Economic Advisers

Export-Import Bank of the United States

Exxon International Company

General Aviation Manufacturers Association

Helicopter Association International

International Civil Aviation Organization

National Aeronautics and Space Administration

National Science Foundation

Office of Management and Budget

U.S. Department of Commerce (Bureau of Economic Analysis; Bureau of the Census; International Trade Administration)

U.S. Department of Defense (Air Force; Army; Ballistic Missile Defense Organization; Comptroller; Directorate for Information, Operations, and Reports; Navy)

U.S. Department of Labor (Bureau of Labor Statistics)

U.S. Department of Transportation (Federal Aviation Administration, Office of Airline Statistics)

CONTENTS

FROM TWO BICYCLE BUILDERS WORKING OUT OF THEIR garage in Ohio to a multinational team building a structure 225 miles above the Earth's surface, the launch and subsequent mating of the first components of the International Space Station (cover) symbolizes the progress mankind has made during the 1900s.

Over the span of less than a century, the aerospace industry has brought amazing progress. Air transportation was born, grew into a dominant form of long-distance travel, and now represents an intricate web of passenger & freight-carrying flying machines. Warfare has been permanently altered; its use and duration, and the misery caused by it, have been significantly reduced. Rocketry, itself a product of warfare, begat spaceflight and space exploration, which has brought satellite communications, remote sensing, and the Global Positioning System to the masses. Clearly, the crowning achievement during the 1900s was stepping onto the Moon and returning safely home—a feat made possible by the work and ingenuity of the U.S. aerospace industry.

Nineteen-ninety-nine may very well be the statistical capstone of the 1900s for the U.S. aerospace industry. A record number of commercial airliners were built; commercial airline traffic (both freight and passenger) reached new highs;

general aviation aircraft billings marked the seventh straight record year; exports, imports, and the resulting trade surplus all reached new highs; industry sales peaked at $151 billion; and profits soared to a record $10 billion in 1999.

However, 1999 was not free of blemishes. Commercial satellites were added to the State Department's Munitions List thereby transferring responsibility for issuing of export licenses away from a legal system designed for export of commercial products to one developed for weapons systems. As a consequence, commercial satellite and parts exports declined by more than 35% and our market share fell from two-thirds to one-half. Federal investment in aerospace R&D in 1998 (latest data available) is 60% less than a decade earlier. In the last two years alone, aerospace employment of R&D-performing scientists and engineers (R&D-S&Es) has fallen 30 percent. As a percentage of national employment of R&D-S&Es, it is at the lowest level on record. Further, the aerospace industry is failing to attract young college graduates into its workforce. The share of aerospace workers in the age bracket 25–34 has fallen ten percentage points (27% to 17%) from 1992 to 1999.

As we stand at the cusp of a new century, we recognize these challenges, but we rightfully take pride in our accomplishments and can't help but gaze into the unimaginable future. Confident in our technical competence, the aerospace industry will assist in building and servicing of the International Space Station, colonize the Moon, and lead man's exploration to Mars and beyond in the next century.

No one knows the advances in medicine that will spawn from the experiments aboard the International Space Station. Nor can we measure the benefits to space travel from our efforts to reduce the transit time to Mars. There is much to be learned! What strides we make in the coming century depend largely upon what we strive to undertake. The good news is America possesses ample imagination and determination to improve and that the U.S. aerospace industry will find the way!

John W. Douglass
President and Chief Executive Officer, Aerospace Industries Association

U.S. AEROSPACE INDUSTRY SALES INCREASED 2.1% IN 1999, following 1998's gain of 12.5%. DoD led with a 5% increase, while NASA and other federal agencies' combined sales fell slightly. Sales to customers other than the U.S. government rose slightly to record levels.

Here are the highlights of the industry's 1999 performance:

Sales

Overall industry sales totaled $151 billion, compared with $148 billion in 1998. U.S. government sales reached $58 billion, up $2.1 billion from the previous year. The "other customers" category rose $464 million to a record $67.5 billion.

As usual, aircraft sector sales led all other product groups. Civil and military sales combined totaled $87 billion, compared with $84 billion in 1998. Total aircraft sales break down into $51 billion for civil and $35 billion for military, with civil aircraft sales dominating military sales for the third time since 1993.

There was also a gain in sales of "related products and services," which surpassed $25 billion, up $517 million from the previous year. Likewise, missile sector sales grew to $8.9 billion, up from $7.7 billion. Unfortunately, space sector sales declined to $30 billion, down from $32 billion in 1998.

For 1999, aerospace industry output amounted to 1.6% of the Gross Domestic Product and 3.5% of U.S. manufacturing sales, down from 1.7% and 3.7% in 1998.

Earnings

Net income after taxes was a record $10.2 billion, up from $7.7 billion in the previous year. As a percentage of sales, the industry's profit amounted to 6.5%, up from the 1998 aerospace profit-to-sales ratio of 5.0%. By comparison, the average for all U.S. manufacturing industries was 6.2%. As a percentage of assets, aerospace earnings amounted to 6.2%; as a percentage of equity, 21.8%.

The consolidated aerospace balance sheet showed net working capital of $11.7 billion, up from $11.5 billion in 1998. Stockholders' equity grew from $43 billion in 1998 to $50 billion in 1999 and total assets climbed substantially from $160 billion to $170 billion.

Orders and Backlog

Net new orders for aerospace products and services rose $4.3 billion, or 3.9%, to $114 billion, up from $110 billion in 1998, reversing the last two years' downward trend. The increase reflects a rise in military orders from $39

billion in 1998 to $51 billion in 1999. Orders in the civil sector fell from $71 billion in 1998 to $64 billion in 1999.

The industry's backlog at year-end 1999 was $190 billion, down from $200 billion in the previous year. Of that, 63%, or $120 billion, are orders for non-military products. The backlog for military systems held steady at $70 billion.

Civil Aircraft Production

U.S. manufacturers shipped 3,477 civil aircraft in 1999 worth a total $45 billion. That represents a gain of 342 units and $3.7 billion in sales over 1998 levels.

Civil transport production—620 aircraft valued at a record $38 billion—accounted for 84% of the total value. These figures compare with 559 aircraft worth $36 billion in 1998.

Production of civil helicopters remained almost even with 1998 at 361 units (down 2) valued at $187 million (down $65 million).

General aviation aircraft sales increased to 2,496 units (up 283) and in dollar value to $6.9 billion (up $1.2 billion). This sales level marked the seventh straight record year for general aviation.

Military Aircraft Production

The Census Bureau reported 1999 sales of military aircraft and parts, including engines, to be $26.3 billion. That figure compares with $23.8 billion in 1998.

The industry produced 333 military aircraft: 107 were delivered to U.S. military agencies and 226 were exported either through Foreign Military Sales arrangements or through direct company-to-foreign-customer sales. The comparable figures for 1998 were 418 total, 149 for the U.S. military services, and 269 exports.

For Fiscal Year (FY) 2000, the major aircraft types procured were: the Air Force C-17 Globemaster III transport, the Navy F/A-18E/F fighter, the Air Force F-22 Raptor fighter, the Navy/Marine Corps V-22 Osprey tiltrotor aircraft, the Army AH-64 Apache helicopter, the Air Force/Navy C-130J Hercules transport, the Navy E-2C Hawkeye early warning and control aircraft, the Air Force E-8C JSTARS surveillance aircraft, the Navy CH-60S helicopter, and the Navy T-45 Goshawk trainer.

Foreign Trade

Aerospace exports remained strong at $62 billion, but declined 2.5% from 1998's all-time high of $64 billion.

The aerospace trade balance also remained healthy although down from 1998's record. Total

imports reached an all-time high of $25 billion, compared with $23 billion in 1998. This resulted in a trade balance of $37 billion, down $3.6 billion or 8.7%.

Civil exports accounted for a majority (81%) of total aerospace exports in 1999. The civil export total of $51 billion compares with $52 billion the previous year, a 2.6% decrease. The largest component of aerospace exports was civil transport aircraft, which at $26 billion accounted for more than half of the civil export total. Jetliner exports were $3.5 billion lower than in the previous year.

Space Programs

Sales of space systems and services came to $30 billion in 1999, down from $32 billion in 1998. AIA figures include civil and military space systems and parts plus U.S. government space activities, including contracts for Research, Development, Test, and Evaluation (RDT&E).

The Census Bureau uses a reporting system that excludes launch vehicle propulsion systems, spacecraft orbital adjustment engines/motors, and RDT&E. The Bureau reported that space systems sales continued a decline which began in 1998, with a total for 1999 of $9 billion, down from $9.5 billion in the previous year. The 1999 sales figure included $3.9 billion in non-military work (commercial plus government-sponsored civil space) and $5.1 billion in military work.

Missile Programs

According to AIA statistics, missile sector sales rose 14.5% in 1999. Missile sector sales amounted to $8.9 billion in 1999, up from $7.7 billion in the previous year. However,

Census Bureau data (which excludes the sale of some propulsion units and RDT&E) showed a smaller rise of 3.8% in the sales of missile systems and parts to $4.5 billion.

DoD outlays for missile procurement began to turn around from the decline that began in FY 1991. Missile outlays for FY 2000 totaled $4.3 billion, up from the FY 1999 figure of $4.1 billion. Another increase in outlays was planned for FY 2001 ($4.5 billion). A significant chunk of funding ($4.3 billion in FY 2000 and $3.9 billion in FY 2001) will go to RDT&E programs related to ballistic missile defense rather than procurement of production-type systems.

Major production programs of 1999/2000 included the Navy Trident II Fleet Ballistic Missile, the Army/Marine Corps Javeline antiarmor missile, the Army/Ballistic Missile Defense Organization Patriot PAC-3 air defense system, and the Army/USMC Hellfire antiarmor missile.

Research and Development

In 1999, total U.S. funding for research and development (R&D) amounted to $245 billion, up from $227 billion in the previous year, according to the National Science Foundation (NSF). Two-thirds of the total (66%) was funded by industry ($162 billion), which also performed the great bulk of R&D work (75%). For 2000, NSF estimated total R&D funding at $264 billion, indicating that industry would again be the principal funding source (68%) and performer (76%).

In 1998 (the latest year for which NSF data was available by industry), aerospace R&D funding totaled $14.4 billion, a decrease of 11% from the previous year. Aerospace industry investment in R&D (federal and company funds) amounted to 9.3% of net sales, down from 11.2% in the previous year. Company funding as a percentage of net sales was 3.3%; the average for all U.S. manufacturing industries was 3.2%.

Employment

Employment in the aerospace industry declined in 1999 after two years of growth. On an annual average employment basis, the industry's labor force fell by 50,000 to a total of 846,000. The 1999 employment figure represented 4.6% of the total employment in all U.S. manufacturing industries. The aerospace workforce also represented 7.6% of total employment by U.S. companies engaged in production of durable goods.

STANDARD INDUSTRIAL CLASSIFICATIONS APPLICABLE TO THE AEROSPACE INDUSTRY

3721 AIRCRAFT
- 37211 Military aircraft
- 37215 Civilian aircraft
- 37217 Modification, conversion, and overhaul of previously accepted aircraft
- 37218 Aeronautical services on complete aircraft, nec

3724 AIRCRAFT ENGINES AND ENGINE PARTS
- 37241 Aircraft engines for military aircraft
- 37242 Aircraft engines for civilian aircraft
- 37243 Aeronautical services on aircraft engines
- 37244 Aircraft engine parts and accessories

3728 AIRCRAFT PARTS AND AUXILIARY EQUIPMENT, NEC
- 37281 Aircraft parts and auxiliary equipment, nec
- 37282 Aircraft propellers and helicopter rotors
- 37283 Research and development on aircraft parts

3761 GUIDED MISSILES AND SPACE VEHICLES
- 37611 Complete guided missiles (excluding propulsion systems)
- 37612 Complete space vehicles (excluding propulsion systems)
- 37613 Research and development on complete guided missiles
- 37614 Research and development on complete space vehicles
- 37615 All other services on complete guided missiles and space vehicles

3663 RADIO AND TELEVISION COMMUNICATIONS EQUIPMENT
- 36631 Communication systems and equipment, except broadcast

3764 SPACE PROPULSION UNITS AND PARTS
- 37645 Complete missile or space vehicle engines and/or propulsion units
- 37646 Research and development on complete missile or space vehicle engines and/or propulsion units
- 37647 Services on complete guided missile or space vehicle engines and/or propulsion units, nec
- 37648 Missile and space vehicle engine and/or propulsion unit parts and accessories

3769 SPACE VEHICLE EQUIPMENT, NEC
- 37692 Missile and space vehicle components, parts and subassemblies, nec
- 37694 Research and development on missile and space vehicle parts and components, nec

3669 COMMUNICATIONS EQUIPMENT, NEC
- 36691 Alarm systems
- 36692 Traffic control equipment
- 36693 Intercommunication equipment

3812 SEARCH, DETECTION, NAVIGATION, GUIDANCE, AERONAUTICAL AND NAUTICAL SYSTEMS, INSTRUMENTS, AND EQUIPMENT
- 38121 Aeronautical, nautical, and navigational instruments, not sending or receiving radio signals
- 38122 Search, detection, navigation, and guidance systems and equipment

3829 MEASURING AND CONTROLLING DEVICES, NEC
- 38291 Aircraft engine instruments, except flight

Source: Office of Management and Budget, "Standard Industrial Classification Manual, 1987."
NOTE: The Standard Industrial Classification (SIC) is a system developed by the U.S. Government to define the industrial composition of the economy, facilitating comparability of statistics. It is revised periodically to reflect the changing industrial composition of the economy.
NEC: Not elsewhere classified.

AEROSPACE INDUSTRY SALES BY CUSTOMER
Calendar Years 1985–1999
(Millions of Dollars)

Year	TOTAL SALES	Aerospace Products and Services				Related Products and Services
		Total	U.S. Government		Other Customers	
			Dept. of Defense	NASA and Other Agencies		

CURRENT DOLLARS

Year	TOTAL SALES	Total	Dept. of Defense	NASA and Other Agencies	Other Customers	Related Products and Services
1985	$ 96,571	$ 80,476	$53,178	$ 6,262	$21,036	$16,095
1986	106,183	88,486	59,161	6,236	23,089	17,697
1987	110,008	91,673	61,817	6,813	23,043	18,335
1988	114,562	95,468	61,327	7,899	26,242	19,094
1989	120,534	100,445	61,199	9,601	29,645	20,089
1990	134,375	111,979	60,502	11,097	40,379	22,396
1991	139,248	116,040	55,922	11,739	48,379	23,208
1992	138,591	115,493	52,202	12,408	50,882	23,099
1993	123,183	102,653	47,017	12,255	43,380	20,531
1994	110,558	92,132	43,795	11,932	36,405	18,426
1995	107,782	89,818	42,401	11,413	36,004	17,964
1996	116,812	97,344	42,535	12,391	42,418	19,469
1997 [r]	131,582	109,651	43,702	12,753	53,196	21,930
1998 [r]	147,991	123,326	42,937	13,343	67,047	24,665
1999	151,095	125,912	45,080	13,322	67,511	25,182

CONSTANT DOLLARS [ar]

Year	TOTAL SALES	Total	Dept. of Defense	NASA and Other Agencies	Other Customers	Related Products and Services
1985	$ 97,843	$ 81,536	$53,878	$ 6,344	$21,313	$16,307
1986	106,396	88,663	59,280	6,248	23,135	17,732
1987	110,008	91,673	61,817	6,813	23,043	18,335
1988	112,869	94,057	60,421	7,782	25,854	18,812
1989	114,250	95,209	58,009	9,100	28,100	19,042
1990	123,734	103,111	55,711	10,218	37,181	20,622
1991	124,998	104,165	50,199	10,538	43,428	20,833
1992	118,555	98,796	44,655	10,614	43,526	19,760
1993	102,482	85,402	39,116	10,196	36,090	17,081
1994	90,104	75,087	35,693	9,725	29,670	15,017
1995	86,572	72,143	34,057	9,167	28,919	14,429
1996	92,196	76,830	33,571	9,780	33,479	15,366
1997	102,959	85,799	34,196	9,979	41,624	17,160
1998	115,348	96,123	33,466	10,400	52,258	19,224
1999	116,766	97,304	34,838	10,295	52,172	19,461

Source: Aerospace Industries Association.
NOTE: See Glossary for explanation of "Aerospace Industry," "Aerospace Sales," "Other Customers," and "Related Products and Services."
   a Based on AIA's aerospace composite price deflator, 1987=100.
   r Revised.

13

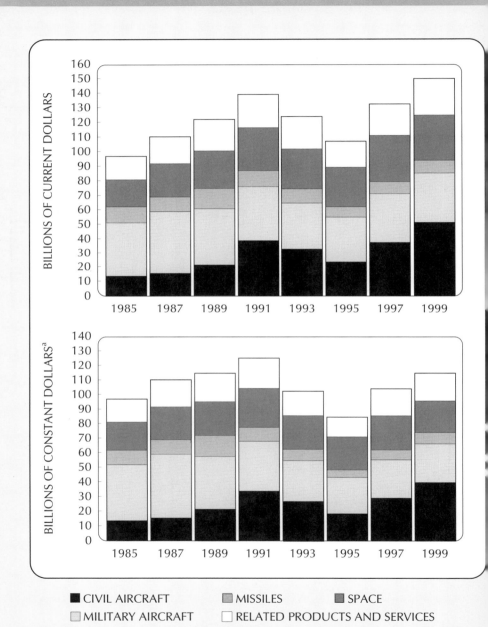

SOURCE: AEROSPACE INDUSTRIES ASSOCIATION
[a] BASED ON AIA'S AEROSPACE COMPOSITE PRICE DEFLATOR (1987=100)

AEROSPACE INDUSTRY SALES BY PRODUCT GROUP
Calendar Years 1985–1999
(Millions of Dollars)

Year	TOTAL SALES	Aircraft			Missiles	Space	Related Products & Services
		Total	Civil	Military			
CURRENT DOLLARS							
1985	$ 96,571	$50,482	$13,730	$36,752	$11,438	$18,556	$16,095
1986	106,183	56,405	15,718	40,687	11,964	20,117	17,697
1987	110,008	59,188	15,465	43,723	10,219	22,266	18,335
1988	114,562	60,886	19,019	41,867	10,270	24,312	19,094
1989	120,534	61,550	21,903	39,646	13,622	25,274	20,089
1990	134,375	71,353	31,262	40,091	14,180	26,446	22,396
1991	139,248	75,918	37,443	38,475	10,970	29,152	23,208
1992	138,591	73,905	39,897	34,008	11,757	29,831	23,099
1993	123,183	65,829	33,116	32,713	8,451	28,372	20,531
1994	110,558	57,648	25,596	32,052	7,563	26,921	18,426
1995	107,782	55,048	23,965	31,082	7,386	27,385	17,964
1996	116,812	60,296	26,869	33,427	8,008	29,040	19,469
1997 [r]	131,582	70,804	37,428	33,376	8,037	30,811	21,930
1998 [r]	147,991	83,951	49,676	34,275	7,730	31,646	24,665
1999	151,095	86,653	51,445	35,208	8,852	30,407	25,182
CONSTANT DOLLARS [ar]							
1985	$ 97,843	$51,147	$13,911	$37,236	$11,589	$18,800	$16,307
1986	106,396	56,518	15,749	40,769	11,988	20,157	17,732
1987	110,008	59,188	15,465	43,723	10,219	22,266	18,335
1988	112,869	59,986	18,738	41,248	10,118	23,953	18,812
1989	114,250	58,341	20,761	37,579	12,912	23,956	19,042
1990	123,734	65,703	28,786	36,916	13,057	24,352	20,622
1991	124,998	68,149	33,611	34,538	9,847	26,169	20,833
1992	118,555	63,221	34,129	29,092	10,057	25,518	19,760
1993	102,482	54,766	27,551	27,215	7,031	23,604	17,081
1994	90,104	46,983	20,861	26,122	6,164	21,941	15,017
1995	86,572	44,215	19,249	24,965	5,933	21,996	14,429
1996	92,196	47,590	21,207	26,383	6,320	22,920	15,366
1997	102,959	55,402	29,286	26,116	6,289	24,109	17,160
1998	115,348	65,433	38,719	26,715	6,025	24,666	19,224
1999	116,766	66,965	39,757	27,209	6,841	23,498	19,461

Source: Aerospace Industries Association.
NOTE: See Glossary for explanation of "Aerospace Industry," "Aerospace Sales," "Other Customers," and "Related Products and Services."
  a Based on AIA's aerospace composite deflator, 1987=100.
  r Revised.

SALES OF MAJOR AEROSPACE COMPANIES
AS REPORTED BY THE BUREAU OF THE CENSUS
Calendar Years 1985–1999
(Millions of Dollars)

Year	GRAND TOTAL	TOTAL		Aircraft, Engines, & Parts		Missiles, Space, & Rocket Propulsion	Other Aerospace		Non-Aerospace
		Military	Non-Mil.	Military	Non-Mil.		Military	Non-Mil.	
CURRENT DOLLARS									
1985	$100,522	$65,098	$35,424	$25,758	$18,182	$16,741	$14,491	$3,675	$21,675
1986	105,577	68,303	37,274	27,043	20,714	17,535	16,287	3,520	20,478
1987	110,301	70,194	40,107	27,806	21,256	20,715	15,786	3,429	21,309
1988	113,548	69,448	44,100	25,068	25,674	21,514	16,382	2,946	21,964
1989	122,148	71,647	50,501	24,287	29,538	22,643	16,908	3,605	25,167
1990	136,646	73,616	63,030	27,667	38,622	22,040	15,773	4,342	28,202
1991	123,862	67,089	56,773	25,385	43,155	23,311	13,472	4,281	14,258
1992	118,736	61,410	57,326	23,509	44,160	21,349	12,153	3,377	14,188
1993	109,926	56,102	53,824	20,099	40,987	18,134	11,936	3,592	15,178
1994	104,296	58,012	46,284	23,652	30,901	18,406	11,981	4,417	14,939
1995	102,797	52,476	50,321	22,944	32,085	18,366	11,921	4,462	13,019
1996	103,115	53,153	49,962	24,804	32,722	18,506	12,171	4,624	10,287
1997	114,946	50,648	64,298	23,944	42,614	21,354	12,320	3,922	10,792
1998 [r]	119,258	45,110	74,148	23,795	52,708	16,109	7,818	5,035	13,796
1999	123,678	49,737	73,942	26,278	56,561	15,661	8,843	3,371	12,964
CONSTANT DOLLARS [ar]									
1985	$101,846	$65,955	$35,891	$26,097	$18,421	$16,961	$14,682	$3,723	$21,960
1986	105,789	68,440	37,349	27,097	20,756	17,570	16,320	3,527	20,519
1987	110,301	70,194	40,107	27,806	21,256	20,715	15,786	3,429	21,309
1988	111,870	68,422	43,448	24,698	25,295	21,196	16,140	2,902	21,639
1989	115,780	67,912	47,868	23,021	27,998	21,463	16,027	3,417	23,855
1990	125,825	67,786	58,039	25,476	35,564	20,295	14,524	3,998	25,969
1991	111,187	60,224	50,963	22,787	38,739	20,925	12,093	3,843	12,799
1992	101,571	52,532	49,038	20,110	37,776	18,263	10,396	2,889	12,137
1993	91,453	46,674	44,779	16,721	34,099	15,087	9,930	2,988	12,627
1994	85,001	47,280	37,721	19,276	25,184	15,001	9,764	3,600	12,175
1995	82,568	42,149	40,418	18,429	25,771	14,752	9,575	3,584	10,457
1996	81,385	41,952	39,433	19,577	25,826	14,606	9,606	3,650	8,119
1997	89,942	39,631	50,311	18,736	33,344	16,709	9,640	3,069	8,444
1998	92,952	35,160	57,793	18,546	41,082	12,556	6,094	3,924	10,753
1999	95,578	38,437	57,142	20,308	43,710	12,103	6,834	2,605	10,019

Source: Bureau of the Census, "Aerospace Industry (Orders, Sales, and Backlog)" Series MA37D (Annually).
 a Based on AIA's aerospace composite price deflator, 1987=100.
 r Revised.

ORDERS AND BACKLOG OF MAJOR AEROSPACE COMPANIES
AS REPORTED BY THE BUREAU OF THE CENSUS
Calendar Years 1985–1999
(Millions of Dollars)

Year	GRAND TOTAL	TOTAL		Aircraft, Engines, & Parts		Missiles, Space, & Rocket Propulsion	Other Aerospace		Non-Aerospace
		Military	Non-Mil.	Military	Non-Mil.		Military	Non-Mil.	
NET NEW ORDERS									
1985	$110,968	$ 70,978	$ 39,990	$28,201	$ 21,471	$20,328	$14,488	$3,042	$23,168
1986	110,836	70,132	40,704	24,124	23,833	20,445	16,836	3,510	22,088
1987	121,224	67,594	53,630	19,347	33,000	26,272	14,178	4,379	24,048
1988	147,128	69,209	77,919	24,242	57,906	20,240	18,423	3,044	23,273
1989	173,635	79,992	93,643	28,818	67,773	26,820	17,814	3,945	28,465
1990	145,965	56,405	89,560	17,735	64,651	20,207	12,945	3,556	26,871
1991	122,485	63,017	59,468	26,675	40,815	24,955	11,329	4,360	14,351
1992	100,306	57,383	42,923	19,631	30,110	22,849	11,201	3,256	13,259
1993	79,770	49,541	30,229	19,518	16,090	14,919	11,121	4,629	13,493
1994	88,706	53,268	35,438	23,352	20,166	13,705	12,924	5,395	13,164
1995	109,109	49,350	59,759	19,854	36,467	19,181	13,716	5,261	14,630
1996	126,267	62,127	64,140	25,343	45,281	27,067	12,136	5,070	11,370
1997	118,993	47,802	71,192	21,424	49,676	21,326	12,348	4,125	10,096
1998 [r]	109,993	38,678	71,314	16,870	47,613	19,699	7,628	4,468	13,715
1999	114,284	50,730	63,553	24,884	46,314	18,435	9,859	2,485	12,307
BACKLOG AS OF DECEMBER 31									
1985	$142,953	$102,244	$ 40,709	$47,893	$ 28,298	$21,410	$19,908	$3,638	$21,806
1986	148,212	104,073	44,139	44,974	31,417	24,320	20,457	3,628	23,416
1987	158,650	99,474	59,176	36,514	43,501	30,544	18,937	4,604	24,550
1988	191,518	99,117	92,401	35,515	75,765	29,078	20,584	4,734	25,842
1989	252,401	114,070	138,331	44,026	115,124	33,771	24,186	7,652	27,642
1990	250,079	88,471	161,608	33,788	139,152	31,648	18,501	4,999	21,991
1991	245,241	89,517	155,724	39,149	134,527	32,657	17,213	4,907	16,788
1992	236,076	92,139	143,937	44,255	124,322	32,933	14,886	4,859	14,821
1993	211,814	91,751	120,063	46,177	96,228	29,511	16,668	7,958	15,272
1994	192,561	84,445	108,116	44,624	85,305	24,746	15,599	8,043	14,244
1995	202,638	82,309	120,329	44,642	92,239	27,113	17,534	8,214	12,906
1996	229,871	89,500	140,371	47,635	106,341	35,440	16,176	9,339	14,940
1997	218,951 [r]	78,870	140,082	43,615	111,931	34,585	12,125	4,754	11,942
1998 [r]	200,288	69,962	130,326	37,530	106,166	31,174	9,665	3,488	12,264
1999	190,094	70,082	120,012	36,214	96,000	32,996	10,423	2,721	11,740

Source: Bureau of the Census, "Aerospace Industry (Orders, Sales, and Backlog)" Series MA37D (Annually).
  r Revised.

AEROSPACE SALES AND THE NATIONAL ECONOMY
Calendar Years 1985–1999
(Billions of Dollars)

Year	Gross Domestic Product[r]	Industry Sales			Aerospace Sales As Percent of		
		Manufac- turing	Durable Goods	Aero- space	GDP	Manufac- turing	Durable Goods
CURRENT DOLLARS							
1985	$4,213.0	$2,332.7	$1,214.5	$ 96.6	2.3%	4.1%	8.0%[r]
1986	4,452.9	2,334.6	1,237.8	106.2	2.4	4.5	8.6
1987	4,742.5	2,474.0	1,296.2	110.0	2.3	4.4	8.5
1988	5,108.3	2,694.0	1,420.5	114.6	2.2[r]	4.3	8.1
1989	5,489.1	2,837.8	1,475.9	120.5	2.2	4.2	8.2
1990	5,803.2	2,909.0	1,483.1	134.4	2.3	4.6	9.1[r]
1991	5,986.2	2,878.8	1,453.2	139.2	2.3[r]	4.8	9.6
1992	6,318.9	3,003.4	1,541.7	138.6	2.2	4.6	9.0
1993	6,642.3	3,125.8	1,629.3	123.2	1.9	3.9	7.6
1994	7,054.3	3,347.3	1,789.3	110.6	1.6	3.3	6.2
1995	7,400.5	3,593.3	1,925.8	107.8	1.5	3.0	5.6
1996	7,813.2	3,713.6	2,002.8	116.8	1.5	3.1	5.8
1997	8,318.4	3,928.3	2,157.7	131.6	1.6	3.3	6.1
1998	8,790.2	4,049.2	2,271.5	148.0	1.7	3.7	6.5
1999	9,299.2	4,258.3	2,408.6	151.1	1.6	3.5	6.3

Year	Gross Domestic Product[r]	Industry Sales			Real Annual Growth[br]			
		Manufac- turing	Durable Goods	Aero- space	GDP	Mfg.	Durs.	Aero.
CONSTANT DOLLARS[ar]								
1985	$5,716.4	$3,165.2	$1,647.9	$ 97.8	3.8%	(1.2)%	0.2%	17.0%
1986	5,913.5	3,100.4	1,643.9	106.4	3.4	(2.0)	(0.2)	8.7
1987	6,111.5	3,188.1	1,670.3	110.0	3.3	2.8	1.6	3.4
1988	6,369.5	3,359.1	1,771.1	112.9	4.2	5.4	6.0	2.6
1989	6,589.6	3,406.7	1,771.8	114.3	3.5	1.4	0.0	1.2
1990	6,708.9	3,363.0	1,714.5	123.7	1.8	(1.3)	(3.2)	8.3
1991	6,673.6	3,209.3	1,620.1	125.0	(0.5)	(4.6)	(5.5)	1.0
1992	6,883.3	3,271.7	1,679.4	118.6	3.1	1.9	3.7	(5.2)
1993	7,058.8	3,321.8	1,731.4	102.5	2.5	1.5	3.1	(13.6)
1994	7,348.2	3,486.8	1,863.8	90.1	4.1	5.0	7.6	(12.1)
1995	7,543.8	3,662.9	1,963.1	86.7	2.7	5.0	5.3	(3.9)
1996	7,813.2	3,713.6	2,002.8	92.2	3.6	1.4	2.0	6.5
1997	8,163.3	3,855.0	2,117.4	103.0	4.5	3.8	5.7	11.7
1998	8,525.9	3,927.5	2,203.2	115.3	4.4	1.9	4.0	12.0
1999	8,890.2	4,071.0	2,302.7	116.8	4.3	3.7	4.5	1.2

Source: Council of Economic Advisors, "Economic Indicators" (Monthly); Bureau of Census; and Aerospace Industries Association.
   a Aerospace industry constant dollar sales based on AIA's aerospace composite price deflator, 1987=100. Others based on GDP deflator, 1996=100.
   b Parentheses indicate negative real annual growth.
   r Revised.

GROSS DOMESTIC PRODUCT,
FEDERAL BUDGET, AND DEFENSE BUDGET
Fiscal Years 1968–2001
(Billions of Dollars)

Year	Fiscal Year GDP[r]	Federal Budget Outlays		Defense Outlays[c] as percent of	
		Net Total[a]	National Defense[b]	GDP[r]	Federal Budget
1968	$ 870.0	$ 178.1	$ 81.9	9.4%	46.0%
1969	949.4	183.6	82.5	8.7	44.9
1970	1,013.7	195.6	81.7	8.1	41.8
1971	1,081.7	210.2	78.9	7.3	37.5
1972	1,178.5	230.7	79.2	6.7	34.3
1973	1,313.6	245.7	76.7	5.8	31.2
1974	1,441.7	269.4	79.3	5.5	29.5
1975	1,559.2	332.3	86.5	5.5	26.0
1976	1,735.9	371.8	89.6	5.2	24.1
Tr.Qtr.	459.2	96.0	22.3	4.8	23.2
1977	1,974.6	409.2	97.2	4.9	23.8
1978	2,219.5	458.7	104.5	4.7	22.8
1979	2,504.9	504.0	116.3	4.6	23.1
1980	2,731.8	590.9	134.0	4.9	22.7
1981	3,060.3	678.2	157.5	5.1	23.2
1982	3,231.1	745.8	185.3	5.7	24.8
1983	3,441.7	808.4	209.9	6.1	26.0
1984	3,846.5	851.9	227.4	5.9	26.7
1985	4,141.6	946.4	252.7[b]	6.1	26.7
1986	4,398.3	990.5	273.4	6.2	27.6
1987	4,653.9	1,004.1	282.0	6.1	28.1
1988	5,016.6	1,064.5	290.4	5.8	27.3
1989	5,406.6	1,143.7	303.6	5.6	26.5
1990	5,738.4	1,253.2	299.3	5.2	23.9
1991	5,927.9	1,324.4	273.3[c]	4.6	20.6
1992	6,221.7	1,381.7	298.4[c]	4.8	21.6
1993	6,560.9	1,409.5[r]	291.1[c]	4.4	20.7
1994	6,948.8	1,461.9[r]	281.6	4.1	19.3
1995	7,322.6	1,515.8[r]	272.1	3.7	17.9
1996	7,700.1	1,560.6[r]	265.8	3.5	17.0
1997	8,182.8	1,601.3[r]	270.5	3.3	16.9
1998	8,636.3	1,652.6	268.5	3.1	16.2
1999	9,115.4	1,703.0	274.9	3.0	16.1
2000[E]	9,571.9	1,789.6	290.6	3.0	16.2
2001[E]	10,041.3	1,835.0	291.2	2.9	15.9

Source: Office of Management and Budget, "The Budget of the United States Government" (Annually).
a "Net Total" is government-wide total less intragovernmental transactions.
b "National Defense" includes the military budget of DoD and other defense-related activities. Beginning in 1985, the Federal Budget reflects establishment of a military retirement trust fund. Data for prior years adjusted for comparable treatment of military retired pay.
c 1991–1993 reflects transfers from the Defense Cooperation Account funded by foreign government and private cash contributions reducing total U.S.-funded military outlays.
E Estimate.
r Revised.
Tr.Qtr. See Glossary.

19

FEDERAL OUTLAYS
DEFENSE, NASA, AND AEROSPACE PRODUCTS & SERVICES
Fiscal Years 1973–2001
(Millions of Dollars)

Year	TOTAL National Defense	TOTAL NASA	Federal Outlays for Aerospace Products & Services			Aerospace as Percent of Total National Defense and NASA
			TOTAL	DoD[a]	NASA	
1973	$ 76,681	$ 3,315	$11,360	$ 8,089	$ 3,271	14.2%
1974	79,347	3,256	11,168	7,987	3,181	13.5
1975	86,509	3,267	11,544	8,373	3,181	12.9
1976	89,619	3,669	12,364	8,816	3,548	13.3
Tr.Qtr.	22,269	951	2,855	1,959	926	12.3
1977	97,241	3,945	13,229	9,389	3,840	13.1
1978	104,495	3,983	13,926	10,067	3,859	12.8
1979	116,342	4,197	16,686	12,622	4,064	13.8
1980	133,995	4,852	20,269	15,558	4,711	14.6
1981	157,513	5,421	24,276	19,002	5,274	14.9
1982	185,309	6,035	29,501	23,575	5,926	15.4
1983	209,903	6,664	35,364	28,808	6,556	16.3
1984	227,413	7,048	39,663	32,723	6,940	16.9
1985	252,748	7,318	44,483	37,335	7,148	17.1
1986	273,375	7,404	49,773	42,558	7,215	17.7
1987	281,999	7,591	51,871	44,429	7,442	17.9
1988	290,361	9,092	48,848	39,922	8,926	16.3
1989	303,559	11,036	52,933	42,072	10,861	16.8
1990	299,331	12,429	53,194	40,992	12,202	17.1
1991[b]	273,292	13,878	53,630	40,089	13,541	18.7
1992[b]	298,350	13,961	50,569	37,085	13,484	16.2
1993[b]	291,086	14,305	45,496	31,763	13,733	14.9
1994	281,642	13,695	41,082	27,774	13,308	13.9
1995	272,066	13,378	36,696	23,638	13,058	12.9
1996	265,753	13,881	32,947	20,530	12,417	11.8
1997	270,505	14,360	32,808	19,888	12,920	11.5
1998	268,456	14,206	33,184	20,380	12,804	11.7
1999	274,873	13,664	32,968	20,564	12,404	11.4
2000[E]	290,636	13,447	32,503	19,955	12,548	10.7
2001[E]	291,202	13,676	34,295	21,589	12,706	11.2

Source: Office of Management and Budget, "The Budget of the United States Government" (Annually); Department of Defense, "Status of Funds" (Annual Summaries); and NASA, "Pocket Statistics" (Annually).

NOTE: "National Defense" includes the military budget of the Department of Defense and other defense-related activities. "TOTAL NASA" includes all categories of the NASA budget; NASA construction is not included in "Aerospace Products and Services." See additional explanation with following table.

a Outlays for aircraft and missile procurement. Does not include RDT&E, which DoD has not reported by product group since 1977, and which, for comparability, has been subtracted from data previously reported in this table for earlier years. Also included are revisions to missile procurement data.

b 1991–1993 reflects transfers from the Defense Cooperation Account funded by foreign government and private cash contributions reducing total U.S.-funded military outlays.

E Estimate. Latest year reflects Administration's budget proposal.

Tr.Qtr. See Glossary.

FEDERAL OUTLAYS FOR AEROSPACE PRODUCTS AND SERVICES
Fiscal Years 1967–2001
(Millions of Dollars)

Year	TOTAL	Department of Defense[a]			NASA[b]
		TOTAL	Aircraft	Missiles	
1967	$15,478	$10,341	$ 8,411	$ 1,930	$ 5,137
1968	16,279	11,681	9,462	2,219	4,598
1969	15,872	11,686	9,177	2,509	4,186
1970	14,559	10,860	7,948	2,912	3,699
1971	12,918	9,580	6,549	3,031	3,338
1972	12,309	8,936	5,927	3,009	3,373
1973	11,360	8,089	5,066	3,023	3,271
1974	11,168	7,987	5,006	2,981	3,181
1975	11,554	8,373	5,484	2,889	3,181
1976	12,364	8,816	6,520	2,296	3,548
Tr.Qtr.	2,885	1,959	1,557	402	926
1977	13,229	9,389	6,608	2,781	3,840
1978	13,926	10,067	6,971	3,096	3,859
1979	16,686	12,622	8,836	3,786	4,064
1980	20,269	15,558	11,124	4,434	4,711
1981	24,276	19,002	13,193	5,809	5,274
1982	29,501	23,575	16,793	6,782	5,926
1983	35,364	28,808	21,013	7,795	6,556
1984	39,663	32,723	23,196	9,527	6,940
1985	44,483	37,335	26,586	10,749	7,148
1986	49,773	42,558	30,828	11,730	7,215
1987	51,871	44,429	32,956	11,473 [c]	7,442
1988	48,848	39,922	28,246	11,676	8,926
1989	52,933	42,072	27,569	14,503	10,861
1990	53,194	40,992	26,142	14,851	12,202
1991	53,630	40,089	25,689	14,400	13,541
1992	50,569	37,085	23,581	13,504	13,484
1993	45,496	31,763	20,359	11,404	13,733
1994	41,082	27,774	18,840	8,934	13,308
1995	36,696	23,638	16,125	7,513	13,058
1996	32,947	20,530	14,331	6,199	12,417
1997	32,808	19,888	14,663	5,225	12,920
1998	33,184	20,380	15,473	4,907	12,804
1999	32,968	20,564	16,484	4,080	12,404
2000 [E]	32,503	19,955	15,666	4,289	12,548
2001 [E]	34,295	21,589	17,100	4,489	12,706

Source: Department of Defense, "Status of Funds" (Annual Summaries); Office of Management and Budget, "The Budget of the United States Government" (Annually); and NASA, "Pocket Statistics" (Annually).

    a Outlays for aircraft and missile procurement. Does not include RDT&E, which DoD has not reported by product group since 1977, and which for comparability, has been subtracted from data previously reported in this table for earlier years.

    b Includes Research & Development and Research & Program Management, and effective with 1984 data, Space Flight, Control, and Data Communications; excludes Construction of Facilities and Air Transportation.

    c Beginning in 1978, DoD combined Navy Missile Procurement with torpedoes and other related products into Navy Weapons Procurement, of which missiles comprise approximately 80 percent.

    E Estimate. Latest year reflects Administration's budget proposal.

Tr.Qtr. See Glossary.

DEPARTMENT OF DEFENSE
TOTAL MILITARY OUTLAYS BY FUNCTIONAL TITLE[a]
Fiscal Years 1992–2001
(Millions of Dollars)

	1992	1993	1994	1995
TOTAL	$286,892[d]	$278,561[d]	$268,622	$259,442
Procurement—TOTAL	$ 74,881	$ 69,936	$ 61,769	$ 54,982
Aircraft	23,581	20,359	18,840	16,125
Missiles[b]	13,504	11,404	8,934	7,513
Ships.....................	11,035	10,136	9,132	8,780
Weapons[b]	3,324	3,061	1,795	1,783
Ammunition.........................	1,996	1,383	997	1,339
Other[c]	21,442	23,593	22,071	19,441
Military Personnel—TOTAL......	81,171	75,904	73,137	70,809
Active Forces	71,433	66,494	63,686	61,606
Reserve Forces.....................	9,738	9,410	9,449	9,203
RDT&E................................	34,632	36,968	34,762	34,594
Operations & Maintenance	91,989	94,094	87,929	91,078
Military Construction..............	4,262	4,831	4,979	6,823
Family Housing	3,271	3,255	3,316	3,571
Other[d]	(3,313)[d]	(6,428)[d]	2,729	(2,415)

Source: Department of Defense, "Status of Funds" (Annual Summaries) and Office of Management and Budget, "The Budget of the United States Government" (Annually).

NOTE: Data in parentheses are credit items. Detail may not add to totals because of rounding.

    a Includes all items in the DoD military budget; excludes the DoD civil budget for the Army Corps of Engineers and other non-defense related activites.

    b Beginning in 1978, DoD combined Navy Missiles Procurement with torpedoes and other related products into Navy Weapons Procurement. Missiles comprise approximately 80 percent of the value of this category.

    c Includes Communications and Electronics.

    d 1991–1993 reflects transfers from the Defense Cooperation Account funded by foreign government and private contributions reducing total U.S.-funded military outlays.

    E Estimate. Latest year reflects Administration's budget proposal.

DEPARTMENT OF DEFENSE
TOTAL MILITARY OUTLAYS BY FUNCTIONAL TITLE[a] (Continued)
Fiscal Years 1992–2001
(Millions of Dollars)

1996	1997	1998	1999	2000 [E]	2001 [E]
$253,187	$258,311	$256,122	$261,380	$277,476	$277,484
$ 48,913	$ 47,690	$ 48,206	$ 48,826	$ 47,972	$ 50,958
14,331	14,663	15,473	16,484	15,666	17,100
6,199	5,225	4,907	4,080	4,289	4,489
7,346	7,085	6,784	6,697	5,823	6,398
1,788	1,918	1,824	1,885	1,684	1,856
1,232	1,615	1,761	1,998	2,014	1,935
18,017	17,184	17,457	17,682	18,496	19,180
66,669	69,724	68,976	69,503	73,509	75,094
57,843	60,371	59,793	59,718	63,449	64,562
8,826	9,353	9,183	9,785	10,060	10,532
36,494	37,015	37,420	37,363	37,400	37,696
88,759	92,461	93,473	96,418	103,821	109,261
6,683	6,187	6,044	5,521	4,767	4,981
3,828	4,003	3,871	3,692	3,753	3,589
1,841	1,231	(1,868)	57	6,254	(4,095)

FEDERAL PRICE DEFLATORS FOR GDP, DEFENSE, PPI, AND CPI
(1972–2001)

Year	GDP[r]		Federal Government Defense Purchases[r]		PPI, Capital Equip-ment	CPI, (Urban) All items
	FY GDP (FY 1996 =100)	CY GDP (CY 1996 =100)	Goods & Services (CY 1996 =100)	Equipment Investment (CY 1996 =100)	(CY 1982 =100)	(CY 82–84 =100)
1972	31.6	31.8	30.6	NA	42.8	41.8
1973	33.2	33.6	32.9	NA	44.2	44.4
1974	35.8	36.6	35.8	NA	50.5	49.3
1975	39.5	40.0	39.2	NA	58.2	53.8
1976	41.9	42.3	42.0	NA	62.1	56.9
1977	44.5	45.0	45.2	NA	66.1	60.6
1978	47.6	48.2	48.3	NA	71.3	65.2
1979	51.4	52.2	52.2	NA	77.5	72.6
1980	56.0	57.1	57.9	NA	85.8	82.4
1981	61.4	62.4	63.7	NA	94.6	90.9
1982	65.7	66.3	68.4	NA	100.0	96.5
1983	68.6	68.9	70.9	NA	102.8	99.6
1984	71.1	71.4	76.0	NA	105.2	103.9
1985	73.5	73.7	77.2	NA	107.5	107.6
1986	75.3	75.3	77.3	NA	109.7	109.6
1987	77.3	77.6	78.0	89.5	111.7	113.6
1988	79.9	80.2	79.7	88.8	114.3	118.3
1989	82.9	83.3	81.9	89.9	118.8	124.0
1990	86.0	86.5	84.6	91.4	122.9	130.7
1991	89.4	89.7	87.7	93.4	126.7	136.2
1992	91.7	91.8	90.8	93.9	129.1	140.3
1993	93.9	94.1	92.5	95.9	131.4	144.5
1994	96.0	96.0	94.5	98.1	134.1	148.2
1995	98.0	98.1	96.9	100.2	136.7	152.4
1996	100.0	100.0	100.0	100.0	138.3	156.9
1997	101.9	101.9	101.2	97.9	138.2	160.5
1998	103.3	103.1	102.0	95.7	137.6	163.0
1999	104.6	104.6	104.8	96.9	137.7	166.6
2000 [E]	105.9	105.9	NA	NA	NA	171.0
2001 [E]	108.0	108.1	NA	NA	NA	175.1

Source: Bureau of Economic Analysis, "Current Business Statistics" (Monthly) and Price Measurement Branch; Council of Economic Advisers, "Economic Report of the President" (Annually); and Office of Management and Budget, "The Budget of the United States Government" (Annually).

E   Estimate.
NA   Not Available.
 r   Revised.
Key: PPI = Producer Price Index for Capital Equipment.
      CPI = Consumer Price Index, All Items, All Urban Consumers for 1978 and subsequent years. Previous years, All Urban Wage Earners.
      GDP = Gross Domestic Product.

PRICE DEFLATORS FOR AEROSPACE INDUSTRY
Calendar Years 1972–1999

Year	Aerospace Deflators (1987 = 100)					
	Composite	SIC 3721	SIC 3724	SIC 3728	SIC 3761	SIC 3764,9
1972	33.7	39.9	30.1	36.6	39.7	34.4
1973	37.7	41.2	30.9	38.1	39.4	35.6
1974	41.5	44.8	34.9	44.0	41.6	40.5
1975	46.6	48.3	42.3	51.6	45.2	49.2
1976	51.0	52.8	45.9	56.5	50.4	53.8
1977	54.6	56.2	49.1	58.7	55.6	58.2
1978	57.5	59.3	54.6	55.2	60.7	63.6
1979	63.5	65.3	60.9	58.9	69.7	70.0
1980	70.6	72.9	66.3	65.3	78.9	78.5
1981	79.5	80.8	77.0	74.9	87.1	89.5
1982	87.9	89.8	85.2	84.3	93.4	97.2
1983	92.2	94.4	89.5	87.9	98.6	101.5
1984	99.8	105.9	98.1	93.6	100.7	102.9
1985 [a]	98.7	100.7	99.2	94.4	102.4	103.2
1986	99.8	100.6	99.3	97.9	103.5	102.4
1987	100.0	100.0	100.0	100.0	100.0	100.0
1988	101.5 [r]	102.2	103.0	103.5	98.6 [r]	98.4 [r]
1989	105.5 [r]	111.0	105.8	106.8	97.1 [r]	97.7 [r]
1990	108.6 [r]	116.8	111.7	109.8	93.4 [r]	98.2 [r]
1991	111.4 [r]	121.3	117.0	113.6	90.5 [r]	101.9 [r]
1992 [b]	116.9 [r]	125.2	122.7	118.0	88.4 [r]	104.8 [r]
1993	120.2 [r]	129.5	124.7	120.9	90.9 [r]	109.6 [r]
1994	122.7 [r]	133.9	128.0	123.5	88.0 [r]	107.1 [r]
1995	124.5 [r]	138.3	129.9	124.4	84.3 [r]	104.2 [r]
1996	126.7 [r]	141.5	132.4	128.8	81.8 [r]	103.6 [r]
1997	127.8 [r]	143.4	133.7	131.4	77.8 [r]	103.4 [r]
1998	128.3 [r]	143.8	134.7	133.0	77.3 [r]	101.7 [r]
1999	129.4	145.1	135.7	134.3	76.9	103.2

Source: Aerospace Industries Association, based on data from: Bureau of Labor Statistics, Producer Price Indices; Bureau of Economic Analysis, Chain-Type Price Indexes and Implicit Price Deflators; and International Trade Administration.
 a The International Trade Administration has discontinued its reporting of the Aerospace Deflators with 1986. Subsequent composite deflators computed by AIA and deflators for 1985 and 1986 revised for consistency.
 b The Bureau of Economic Analysis discontinued its reporting in 1995 of the National Defense Purchases Deflators (used in AIA's Composite calculations). 1992-1994 revised using 1992 fixed weights and BEA's Chain-Type Price Indexes for National Defense Investment and Consumption Expenditures.
 E Estimated.
 r Revised.
Key: SIC = Standard Industrial Classification, SIC 3721 = Aircraft; SIC 3724 = Aircraft Engines and Engine Parts; SIC 3728 = Aircraft Parts; SIC 3761 = Missiles and Space Vehicles; SIC 3764 = Space Propulsion; SIC 3769 = Space Equipment not elsewhere classified.

SALES OF AIRCRAFT, ENGINES, AND PARTS REMAINED STRONG in 1999, with growth in both military and non-military spending. Census Bureau data reported aircraft sector sales totaled $83 billion, an increase of 8.3% over 1998's $77 billion.

Gains of almost $3.9 billion, or 7.3%, in non-military sales to $57 billion and $2.5 billion (10%) in military sales to $26 billion drove the increase. The overall picture, in inflation-adjusted constant dollars, showed aircraft sector sales growth for the fourth consecutive year following a four-year decline.

Census figures showed a 10% increase in new orders for aircraft, engines, and parts in 1999, due entirely to military orders. Total orders came to $71 billion, up from $64 billion for the previous year. Military orders rose from $17 billion to $25 billion in 1999, while non-military orders fell from $48 billion to $46 billion.

The backlog at year-end 1999 was $132 billion, down from $144 billion at year-end 1998. The decline in the unfilled order backlog was largely driven by non-military orders for complete civil aircraft and parts, which fell from $94 billion in 1998 to $83 billion. The order backlog for engines and engine parts grew 5.1% to $15 billion.

The largest component of the "non-military" sales category is complete civil aircraft with 1999 shipments of 3,477—342 higher than the previous year. That total breaks down into 620 commercial transports (up 61), 361 helicopters (down 2), and 2,496 general aviation aircraft (up 283). In dollar terms, 84% of the total value of shipments was for transport aircraft (i.e., $38 billion out of $45 billion). Helicopter sales came to $187 million, down from $252 million in 1998, and general aviation aircraft sales climbed to $6.9 billion, up from $5.6 billion, marking another record-high year for that category.

The backlog of unfilled orders for civil transports decreased in 1999 following four years of growth. At year-end 1999, the number of airliners on backlog was 1,512—down from 1,786.

Military aircraft production for 1999 amounted to 333 units. Of that total, 226 were exported and only 107 were built for U.S. military agencies. The comparable figures for 1998 were 418 total, 269 exports, and 149 for the U.S. military services.

For FY 2000, the largest military aircraft procurement was $3.4 billion for 15 C-17 Globemaster III transports for the Air Force. Other major procurements included: $2.8 billion for 36 Navy F/A-18E/F fighters, $964 million for 11 Navy/Marine Corps V-22 Ospreys,

$781 million for Army AH-64 Apache helicopters, $383 million for three Navy E-2C Hawkeye early warning and control aircraft, $358 million for 17 Navy CH-60S helicopters, $333 million for 15 Navy T-45 Goshawk trainers, $301 million for 11 Navy/Marine Corps AV-8B Harrier V/STOL fighters, $292 million for five Air Force F-15E Eagle fighters, and $288 million for one USAF E-8C JSTARS surveillance aircraft.

The principal procurements planned for FY 2001 were $2.9 billion for 42 F/A-18E/Fs, $2.9 billion for 12 C-17 Globemasters, $2.6 billion for 10 Air Force F-22 Raptors, $1.6 billion for 16 Navy/Marine Corps V-22 Ospreys, and $745 million for Army Apaches.

SALES OF AIRCRAFT, ENGINES, AND PARTS
Calendar Years 1985–1999
(Millions of Dollars)

Year	GRAND TOTAL	TOTAL		Complete Aircraft & Parts		Aircraft Engines & Parts	
		Mili-tary	Non-Mil.	Mili-tary	Non-Mil.	Mili-tary	Non-Mil.
CURRENT DOLLARS							
1985	$43,940	$25,758	$18,182	$21,642	$12,607	$4,116	$ 5,575
1986	47,757	27,043	20,714	23,089	14,876	3,954	5,838
1987	49,062	27,806	21,256	22,168	14,862	5,638	6,394
1988	50,742	25,068	25,674	19,030	16,681	6,038	8,993
1989	53,825	24,287	29,538	18,256	20,140	6,031	9,398
1990	66,289	27,667	38,622	22,023	27,872	5,644	10,750
1991	68,540	25,385	43,155	19,710	33,215	5,675	9,940
1992	67,669	23,509	44,160	18,411	35,595	5,098	8,565
1993	61,086	20,099	40,987	16,118	32,780	3,981	8,207
1994	54,553	23,652	30,901	20,127	23,176	3,525	7,725
1995	55,029	22,944	32,085	19,596	22,897	3,348	9,188
1996	57,526	24,804	32,722	20,822	20,993	3,982	11,729
1997	66,558	23,944	42,614	21,297	33,206	2,647	9,408
1998[r]	76,503	23,795	52,708	21,154	42,541	2,641	10,167
1999	82,839	26,278	56,561	23,124	45,217	3,154	11,344
CONSTANT DOLLARS [ar]							
1985	$44,519	$26,097	$18,421	$21,927	$12,773	$4,170	$ 5,648
1986	47,853	27,097	20,756	23,135	14,906	3,962	5,850
1987	49,062	27,806	21,256	22,168	14,862	5,638	6,394
1988	49,992	24,698	25,295	18,749	16,434	5,949	8,860
1989	51,019	23,021	27,998	17,304	19,090	5,717	8,908
1990	61,040	25,476	35,564	20,279	25,665	5,197	9,899
1991	61,526	22,787	38,739	17,693	29,816	5,094	8,923
1992	57,886	20,110	37,776	15,749	30,449	4,361	7,327
1993	50,820	16,721	34,099	13,409	27,271	3,312	6,828
1994	44,460	19,276	25,184	16,403	18,888	2,873	6,296
1995	44,200	18,429	25,771	15,740	18,391	2,689	7,380
1996	45,403	19,577	25,826	16,434	16,569	3,143	9,257
1997	52,080	18,736	33,344	16,664	25,983	2,071	7,362
1998	59,628	18,546	41,082	16,488	33,157	2,058	7,924
1999	64,018	20,308	43,710	17,870	34,944	2,437	8,767

Source: Bureau of the Census, "Aerospace Industry (Orders, Sales, and Backlog)" Series MA37D (Annually).
  a Based on AIA's aerospace composite price deflator, 1987=100.
  r Revised.

ORDERS AND BACKLOG OF AIRCRAFT, ENGINES, AND PARTS
Calendar Years 1985–1999
(Millions of Current Dollars)

Year	GRAND TOTAL	TOTAL		Complete Aircraft & Parts		Aircraft Engines & Parts	
		Military	Non-Mil.	Military	Non-Mil.	Military	Non-Mil.
NET NEW ORDERS							
1985	$ 49,942	$28,201	$ 21,741	$24,526	$ 15,689	$3,675	$ 6,052
1986	47,957	24,124	23,833	19,852	17,592	4,272	6,241
1987	52,347	19,347	33,000	15,070	24,083	4,277	8,917
1988	82,148	24,242	57,906	17,493	41,762	6,749	16,144
1989	96,591	28,818	67,773	23,569	52,619	5,249	15,154
1990	82,386	17,735	64,651	12,766	52,371	4,969	12,280
1991	67,490	26,675	40,815	22,140	30,745	4,535	10,070
1992	49,741	19,631	30,110	16,391	20,548	3,240	9,562
1993	35,608	19,518	16,090	15,853	11,238	3,665	4,852
1994	43,518	23,352	20,166	19,806	12,854	3,546	7,312
1995	56,321	19,854	36,467	16,248	27,156	3,606	9,311
1996	70,624	25,343	45,281	21,755	33,802	3,588	11,479
1997	71,100	21,424	49,676	19,102	41,439	2,322	8,237
1998 r	64,483	16,870	47,613	14,051	37,362	2,819	10,251
1999	71,198	24,884	46,314	21,554	34,523	3,330	11,791
BACKLOG AS OF DECEMBER 31							
1985	$ 76,191	$47,893	$ 28,298	$40,205	$ 22,348	$7,688	$ 5,950
1986	76,391	44,974	31,417	36,968	25,064	8,006	6,353
1987	80,015	36,514	43,501	29,869	34,625	6,645	8,876
1988	111,280	35,515	75,765	28,186	59,679	7,329	16,086
1989	159,150	44,026	115,124	36,888	95,108	7,138	20,016
1990	172,940	33,788	139,152	27,259	119,123	6,529	20,029
1991	173,676	39,149	134,527	32,795	116,139	6,354	18,388
1992	168,577	44,255	124,322	39,748	107,686	4,507	16,636
1993	142,405	46,177	96,228	41,732	82,772	4,445	13,456
1994	129,929	44,624	85,305	40,206	72,295	4,418	13,010
1995	136,871	44,642	92,229	39,673	77,802	4,969	14,427
1996	153,976	47,635	106,341	42,788	91,851	4,847	14,490
1997	155,546	43,615	111,931	40,562	100,022	3,053	11,909
1998 r	143,696	37,530	106,166	34,866	94,161	2,664	12,005
1999	132,214	36,214	96,000	33,364	83,437	2,850	12,563

Source: Bureau of the Census, "Aerospace Industry (Orders, Sales, and Backlog)" Series MA37D (Annually).
   r Revised.

U.S. AIRCRAFT PRODUCTION—CIVIL
Calendar Years 1969-1999

Year	TOTAL	Domestic Shipments			Export Shipments		
		Trans-ports	Heli-copters	General Aviation	Trans-ports	Heli-copters	General Aviation
1969	13,505	332	282	9,996	182	252	2,461
1970	8,076	127	150	5,246	184	332	2,037
1971	8,158	50	171	5,900	173	298	1,566
1972	10,576	79	319	7,702	148	256	2,072
1973	14,709	143	342	10,482	151	428	3,163
1974	15,326	91	433	9,903	241	395	4,263
1975	15,251	127	528	10,804	188	336	3,268
1976	16,429	64 [a]	442	12,232	158	315	3,218
1977	17,913	54	527	13,441	101	321	3,469
1978	18,962	130	536	14,346	111	368	3,471
1979	18,460	176	570	13,177	200	459	3,878
1980	13,634	150	841	8,703	237	525	3,178
1981	10,916	132	619	6,840	255	453	2,617
1982	5,085	111	333	3,326	121	254	940
1983	3,356	133	187	2,172	129	216	519
1984	2,999	102	143	2,013	83	233	425
1985	2,691	126	247	1,545	152	137	484
1986	2,156	171	120	1,031	159	210	464
1987	1,800	187	116	598	170	242	487
1988	1,949	206	103	500	217	280	643
1989	2,448	138	221	225	260	294	1,310
1990	2,268	215	254	335	306	349	809
1991	2,181	204	253	487	385	318	534
1992	1,790	180	112	541	387	212	358
1993	1,630	130	83	631	278	175	333
1994	1,545	87	154	543	222	154	385
1995	1,625	119	82	714	137	210	363
1996	1,677	97	64	747	172	214	383
1997	2,289	122	87	1,160	252	259	409
1998	3,135	184	125	1,814	375	238	399
1999	3,477	279	180	1,993	341	181	503

Source: Aerospace Industries Association, based on company reports; General Aviation Manufacturers Association; and Department of Commerce, International Trade Administration.

a Prior to 1976, includes the C-130 military transport.

U.S. AIRCRAFT PRODUCTION—MILITARY
Calendar Years 1969–1999

Year	TOTAL	U.S. Military Agencies	Exports		
			Total	FMS[a]	Direct[b]
1969	4,290	3,644	646	NA	NA
1970	3,720	3,085	635	NA	NA
1971	2,914	2,232	682	NA	NA
1972	2,530	1,993	537	124	413
1973	1,821	1,243	578	129	449
1974	1,513	799	714	365	349
1975	1,779	844	935	525	410
1976	1,318	625	693	518	175
1977	1,134	454	680	408	272
1978	996	467	529	256	273
1979	837	531	306	203	103
1980	1,047	625	422	194	228
1981	1,062	703	359	215	144
1982	1,159	690	469	68	401
1983	1,053	766	287	70	217
1984	936	561	375	71	304
1985	919	643	276	134	142
1986	1,107	708	399	110	289
1987	1,210	725	485	133	352
1988	1,305	687	618	138	480
1989	1,261	614	647	92	555
1990	1,053	664	387	99	290
1991	911	556	355	94	261
1992	753	422	331	122	209
1993	955[c]	437	518	146	372[c]
1994	764	418	346	69	277
1995	811[d]	354	457	108	349
1996	558	242	316	106	210
1997	488	151	337	181	156
1998[r]	418	149	269	175	94
1999	333	107	226	114	112

Source: Aerospace Industries Association, based on USAF, USN, and USA survey responses and Department of Commerce, International Trade Administration.
a Also includes acceptances of NATO AWACS aircraft.
b Military aircraft exported via commercial contracts, directly from manufacturers to foreign governments.
c The number of small (450 kg–2000 kg), new aircraft exported doubled in 1993 to 340 worth $18 million.
d Includes 358 small (450 kg–2000 kg), new aircraft worth $14.7 million.
NA Not available.
r Revised.

CIVIL AIRCRAFT SHIPMENTS
Calendar Years 1985–1999

Year	TOTAL	Transport Aircraft[a]	Helicopters	General Aviation
NUMBER OF AIRCRAFT SHIPPED				
1985	2,691	278	384	2,029
1986	2,155	330	330	1,495
1987	1,800	357	358	1,085
1988	1,949	423	383	1,143
1989	2,448	398	515	1,535
1990	2,268	521	603	1,144
1991	2,181	589	571	1,021
1992	1,790	567	324	899
1993	1,630	408	258	964
1994	1,545	309	308	928
1995	1,625	256	292	1,077
1996	1,677	269	278	1,130
1997	2,289	374	346	1,569
1998	3,135	559	363	2,213
1999	3,477	620	361	2,496
VALUE—Millions of Dollars				
1985	$10,385	$ 8,448	$506	$1,431
1986	11,858	10,308	288	1,262
1987	12,148	10,507	277	1,364
1988	15,855	13,603	334	1,918
1989	17,129	15,074	251	1,804
1990	24,477	22,215	254	2,008
1991	29,035	26,856	211	1,968
1992	30,728	28,750	142	1,836
1993	26,389	24,133	113	2,144
1994	20,666	18,124[E]	185	2,357
1995	18,299	15,263[E]	194	2,842
1996	20,884	17,564[E]	193	3,127
1997	31,834	26,929	231	4,674
1998	41,444	35,545	252	5,646
1999	45,187	38,105	187	6,895

Source: Aerospace Industries Association, based on company reports and General Aviation Manufacturers' Association.
   a U.S.-manufactured fixed-wing aircraft over 33,000 pounds empty weight, including all jet transports plus the four-engine turboprop-powered Lockheed L-100.
   E Estimated.

CIVIL TRANSPORT AIRCRAFT BACKLOG[a]
As of December 31, 1995–1999

Company and Model	1995	1996	1997	1998	1999
TOTAL AIRCRAFT ON ORDER					
(Domestic and Foreign Orders)	1,291	1,617	1,744	1,786	1,512[b]
Value (Millions of Dollars)	NA	NA	$93,788	$86,057	$72,972
Boeing—TOTAL.....................	1,079	1,418	1,602	1,595	1,385
B-737	491	764	909	978	916
B-747	121	161	159	102	77
B-757	132	134	133	130	81
B-767	118	86	141	134	122
B-777	217	273	260	251	189
Douglas[c]—TOTAL..................	212	199	142	191	127
MD-11	21	15	14	14	6
MD-80/90	141	134	78	62	3
MD-95 (B-717)	50	50	50	115	118
TOTAL FOREIGN ORDERS	701	753	790	687	493
Value (Millions of Dollars)	NA	NA	$51,583[E]	$38,726[E]	$29,939[E]
Boeing—TOTAL.....................	570	637	709	625	458
B-737	199	234	336	344	258
B-747	112	133	122	75	65
B-757	21	25	38	40	15
B-767	58	38	29	21	14
B-777	180	207	184	145	106
Douglas[c]—TOTAL..................	131	116	81	62	35
MD-11	14	14	13	11	6
MD-80/90	117	102	68	36	3
MD-95 (B-717)	—	—	—	15	26

Source: Aerospace Industries Association, based on company reports.
NOTE: Boeing's unfilled orders not reported on a firm order basis.
a Unfilled firm orders excluding options for U.S.-manufactured transport aircraft over 33,000 pounds. Includes new transports contracted for lease from the manufacturer.
b Includes 84 unidentified orders.
c Formerly reported as McDonnell Douglas.
E Estimate.
NA Not available.

SHIPMENTS OF CIVIL TRANSPORT AIRCRAFT[a]
Calendar Years 1995–1999

Company and Model	1995	1996	1997	1998	1999
TOTAL					
Number of Aircraft Shipped	256	269	374	559	620
Value (Millions of Dollars)	$15,263[E]	$18,915[E]	$26,929	$35,545	$38,105
Boeing—TOTAL....................	206	218	320	505	561
B-737	89	76	135	281	320
B-747	25	26	39	53	47
B-757	43	42	46	50	67
B-767	36	42	41	47	44
B-777	13	32	59	74	83
Douglas[b]—TOTAL.................	50	51	54	54	59
MD-11	18	15	12	12	8
MD-80	18	12	16	8	26
MD-90	14	24	26	34	13
MD-95 (B-717)	—	—	—	—	12

Source: Aerospace Industries Association, based on company reports.
   a   U.S.-manufactured fixed-wing aircraft over 33,000 lbs.
   b   Formerly reported as McDonnell Douglas.
   E   Estimated.

SPECIFICATIONS OF U.S. CIVIL JET TRANSPORT AIRCRAFT[a]
On Order or in Production as of 1999

Number of Engines and Crew, and Model Designation[b]	Initial Service	Standard Mixed Class	Operating Empty Weight (000's lbs)	Maximum Takeoff Gross Weight (000's lbs)	Range (Nautical Miles)[c]	Engine Manufacturer[d] and Model
FOUR ENGINES/CREW OF 2						
747-400*	1989	416-524	399	875	7,325	GE CF6-80C2, P&W PW4000, or RR RB211-524
TWO ENGINES/CREW OF 2						
MD-83	1985	144-172	81	160	2,346	P&W JT8D-219
MD-90	1995	152-172	90	156	1,912	IAE V2500-D5
MD-95 (717)	1999	106	70	121	1,375	BMW-RR BR715
737-300	1984	128-149	72	139	2,255	CFMI CFM56-3C-1
737-400	1988	146-168	76	150	2,059	CFMI CFM56-3C-1
737-500	1990	110-132	70	134	2,059	CFMI CFM56-3C-1
737-600	1998	110-132	80	144	3,050	CFMI CFM56-7B
737-700	1997	126-149	83	155	3,260	CFMI CFM56-7B
737-800	1998	162-189	91	174	2,940	CFMI CFM56-7B
737-900	2001	177-189	95	174	2,745	CFMI CFM56-7B
757-200	1983	192-239	129	255	3,928	RR RB211-535 or P&W PW2000
757-300	1999	239-289	141	273	3,467	RR RB211-535 or P&W PW2000
767-200ER*	1984	181-285	190	395	5,737	P&W PW4000 or GE CF6-80C2
767-300*	1986	218-351	200	412	5,344	P&W PW4000 , GE CF6-80C2, or RR RB211-514
767-300ER*	1997	218-351	203	412	5,344	P&W PW4000, GE CF6-80C2, or RR RB211-514
767-400*	2000	245-375	229 227	450	5,635	P&W PW4000 or GE CF6-80C2
777-200*	1995	320-440	310	545	5,149	RR Trent, GE GE90, or P&W PW4000
777-200ER*	1997	320-440	314	656	7,700	RR Trent, GE GE90, or P&W PW4000
777-300*	1998	386-550	352	660	5,960	RR Trent or P&W PW4000

Source: Aerospace Industries Association, based on company reports.
  a All jet-powered passenger transport aircraft 33,000 pounds or more empty weight.
  b The Boeing Company manufacturers models: 737, 747, 757, 767, & 777 and its Douglas Products Division manufacturers models: MD-80, MD-90, and MD-95 (renamed the 717).
  c Full passenger load and baggage.
  d P&W = Pratt & Whitney; GE = General Electric; RR = Rolls-Royce; CFMI = General Electric/Snecma; IAE = International Aero Engines; BMW = Bayerische Motoren Werke.
  * Wide-body aircraft.

SPECIFICATIONS OF U.S. CIVIL HELICOPTERS
In Production as of 1999

Company	Commercial Model	Number of Places	Useful Load (Lbs.)	Range with Useful Load (N.Miles)	External Cargo Payload (Lbs.)
Brantly International	B-2B	2	650	217	—
Enstrom Helicopter	F-28 Series	3	1,030	241	1,000
	280 Series	3	1,015	260	1,000
	480 Series	5	1,175	375	1,000
Hiller Aircraft	UH-12E3	3	1,341	232	1,000
	UH-12E3T	3	1,460	172	1,000
Kaman	K-1200	1	500	267	6,855
MD Helicopters	500 Series	5	1,519	264	2,069
	520 Series	5	1,764	210	2,364
	530F	5	1,509	232	2,159
	600 Series	8	2,000	380	2,720
	900 Series	8	2,975	303	3,000
Robinson Helicopter	R22	2	531	180	—
	R44	4	980	365	—
Schweizer Aircraft	300C	3	950	201	1,050
	300CB	2	662	NA	—
	330	4	1,120	300	—
Sikorsky Aircraft	S-76C	14	4,813	439	3,300

Source: Helicopter Association International, "2000 Helicopter Annual" (Annually).
   NA   Not available.

CIVIL HELICOPTER SHIPMENTS[a]
Calendar Years 1995–1999

Company and Model	1995	1996	1997	1998	1999
CIVIL SHIPMENTS..................	292	278	346	363	361
Value (Millions of Dollars) ...	$194	$193	$231	$252	$187
Brantly—TOTAL	—	—	—	2	—
B-2B	—	—	—	2	—
Enstrom—TOTAL	11	11	12	14	8
F-28/280 series	3	4	5	3	5
480 series...........................	8	7	7	11	3
Hiller[b]—TOTAL	1	1	—	—	—
UH12E	1	1	—	—	—
Kaman—TOTAL.....................	6	8	4	2	—
K-1200	6	8	4	2	—
MD Helicopters[c]—TOTAL	34	29	27	37	33
500 series..........................	12	9	9	5	5
520N series	10	5	2	2	5
530 series..........................	—	—	—	5	6
600 series..........................	—	—	15	21	6
900 series..........................	12	15	1	4	11
Robinson—TOTAL.................	179	164	246	251	278
R22	83	86	132	117	128
R44	96	78	114	134	150
Schweizer—TOTAL	47	56	39	41	35
300C................................	22	20	15	17	23
300CB	21	31	19	21	11
330	4	5	5	3	1
Sikorsky—TOTAL	14	9	18	16	7
S-76	14	9	18	16	7

Source: Aerospace Industries Association, based on company reports.
NOTE: All data exclude production by foreign licensees.
  a Domestic and export helicopter shipments for non-military use. Helicopters in military configuration exported to foreign governments and purchased under commercial contract are reported elsewhere. Models which may be shipped in either a civil or a military configuration appear in both tables. Please note that shipments from Bell Helicopter's Canadian facilities are excluded as are other foreign-produced helicopters, but reported separately below for information purposes only.
  b Formerly reported as Rogerson.
  c Formerly reported as McDonnell Douglas.

Bell—TOTAL	159	212	233	197	146
206B...............................	63	44	35	24	28
206L/LT	48	31	13	16	12
212	15	13	1	1	—
230	10	—	2	2	—
407	—	87	138	104	62
412	23	24	36	35	26
430	—	13	8	15	18

DIRECT EXPORT SHIPMENTS OF MILITARY HELICOPTERS[a]
Calendar Years 1995–1999

Manufacturer and Model	1995	1996	1997	1998	1999
DIRECT MILITARY EXPORT **SHIPMENTS**	21	8	25	50	28
Value (Millions of Dollars)	$142	$131	$213	$757	$484
Boeing Vertol CH-47/414/352	2	7	1	17	10
Hiller UH-12E	—	—	2	—	—
McDonnell Douglas AH-64	—	—	—	1	6
Sikorsky S-70C	19	1	22	32	12

Source: Aerospace Industries Association, company reports.
  a Shipments of helicopters in military configuration exported directly from U.S. manufacturers to foreign governments. Military helicopters exported via Foreign Military Sales (FMS) are reported with Dept. of Defense (DoD) aircraft acceptance data elsewhere in this chapter. Some models reported on this page may be shipped in either military or civil configuration; see Civil Helicopter Shipments table for additional data.

GENERAL AVIATION AIRCRAFT SHIPMENTS
By Selected Manufacturers
Calendar Years 1995–1999

	1995	1996	1997	1998	1999
NUMBER OF AIRCRAFT SHIPPED	1,077	1,130	1,569	2,213	2,496
Single-Engine, Piston	515	530	905	1,436	1,635
Multi-Engine, Piston	61	70	80	98	112
Turboprop	255	289	236	271	264
Turbojet	246	241	348	408	485
VALUE OF SHIPMENTS[a] (Millions of Dollars)	$2,842	$3,127	$4,674	$5,647	$6,895
Piston	$ 123	$ 146	$ 214	$ 337	$ 385
Turboprop	653	734	740	778	658
Turbojet	2,066	2,247	3,720	4,532	5,852
Number of Aircraft By Selected Manufacturer					
American Champion	46	53	46	74	91
Aviat	42	56	61	85	83
Bellanca	1	2	2	1	1
Cessna	200	229	612	1,072	1,202
Cirrus Design	—	—	—	—	9
Classic	7	6	6	—	—
Commander	25	15	14	13	13
Fairchild	7	7	—	—	—
Gulfstream	26	27	51	61	70
Learjet	43	34	45	61	99
Maule	68	63	54	63	69
Mooney	84	73	86	93	97
Piper	165	183	222	295	341
Raytheon[b]	363	382	370	395	421

Source: General Aviation Manufacturers' Association.
  a Manufacturers' net billing price.
  b Formerly reported as Beech.

MILITARY AIRCRAFT ACCEPTED BY U.S. MILITARY AGENCIES
Number and Flyaway Value
Calendar Years 1985–1999

Year	TOTAL	Bomber/ Patrol/ Command/ Control	Fighter/ Attack	Trans- port/ Tanker	Trainer	Heli- copter	Other
NUMBER							
1985	777	34	409	25	—	306	3
1986	818	52	424	76	—	266	—
1987	858	74	483	36	—	265	—
1988	842	55	509	31	—	247	—
1989	706	24	408	21	—	253	—
1990	763	24	454	25	—	260	—
1991	650	17	395	23	—	215	—
1992	544	10	312	30	37	155	—
1993	583	11	293	25	56	198	—
1994	487	6	167	40	114	157	3
1995	462	4	133	32	102	176	15
1996	348	4	116	28	54	146	—
1997	332	4	202	19	26	81	—
1998	324[r]	10	188	30[r]	33	63[r]	—
1999	221	6	142	32	12	29	—
FLYAWAY VALUE—Millions of Dollars							
1985	$14,122	$3,640	$7,923	$ 838	$ —	$1,715	$ 6
1986	20,903	8,177	8,004	2,665	—	2,057	—
1987	21,459	8,569	8,900	2,218	—	1,772	—
1988	16,031	2,911	8,953	2,314	—	1,853	—
1989	11,968	1,423	7,735	743	—	2,067	—
1990	13,036	1,499	8,731	605	—	2,201	—
1991	11,754	1,023	8,517	437	—	1,777	—
1992	11,482	613	7,673	1,346	267	1,583	—
1993	12,101	1,530	6,400	1,553	484	2,134	—
1994	13,000	3,861	3,661	3,298	477	1,686	17
1995	12,369	3,585	3,547	2,759	460	1,922	98
1996	11,383	3,596	3,524	2,350	337	1,576	—
1997	10,945	1,921	5,653	2,336	270	766	—
1998[r]	15,099	4,831	6,240	2,890	319	835	—
1999	9,129	415	4,544	3,636	216	318	—

Source: Aerospace Industries Association, based on USAF, USN, and USA survey responses.
NOTE: Data represent new U.S.-manufactured aircraft, excluding gliders and targets. Values include spares, spare parts, and support equipment that are procured with the aircraft. Includes aircraft accepted for shipment to foreign governments for military assistance programs and foreign military sales.
r Revised.

MILITARY AIRCRAFT ACCEPTANCES BY UNITED STATES AIR FORCE[a]
Calendar Years 1998–1999
(Costs in Millions of Dollars)

Type and Model	Number		Flyaway Cost[b]		Weapon System Cost[c]	
	1998	1999	1998	1999	1998	1999
AIR FORCE—TOTAL............	23[r]	44	$7,349[r]	$3,848	$9,252[r]	$4,284
Bomber—TOTAL	5	—	$4,501	$ —	$5,985	$ —
B-2	5	—	4,501	—	5,985	—
Fighter/Attack—TOTAL	1	17	20	633	25	692
F-15	—	12	—	533	—	569
F-16	1	5	20	100	25	123
Transports/Tankers—TOTAL	17[r]	27	2,829[r]	3,215	3,243[r]	3,592
C-17	10	11	2,434	2,486	2,843	2,772
C-32	4	—	338	—	338	—
C-37	1[r]	2	36[r]	76	41[r]	86
C-38	2	—	21	—	21	—
C-130 variants	—	14	—	653	—	734

Source: Department of the Air Force.
a   Air Force acceptances for own use; excludes FMS/MAP shipments.
b   Flyaway Cost includes airframe, engines, electronics, communications, armament, other installed equipment, and non-recurring costs associated with the manufacture of aircraft.
c   Weapon system cost includes flyaway costs, peculiar ground equipment, training equipment, and technical data.
r   Revised.

MILITARY AIRCRAFT ACCEPTANCES BY UNITED STATES ARMY[a]
Calendar Years 1998–1999

Type and Model	Number		Flyaway Cost[b]		Weapon System Cost[c]	
	1998	1999	1998	1999	1998	1999
ARMY—TOTAL	54	26	$444[r]	$215	$492[r]	$244
Helicopters—TOTAL...........	41	21	$383[r]	$192	$431[r]	$221
UH-60L	41	21	383[r]	192	431[r]	221
Transports/Tankers—TOTAL	13	5	61	23	61	23
C-23	8	—	41	—	41	—
UC-35	5	5	21	23	21	23

Source: Department of the Army.
a   Army acceptances for own use; excludes FMS/MAP shipments.
b   Flyaway cost includes airframes, engines, electronics, communications, armament and other installed equipment.
c   Weapon System Cost includes flyaway cost, initial spares, ground equipment, training equipment and other support items.
r   Revised.

MILITARY AIRCRAFT ACCEPTANCES BY UNITED STATES NAVY[a]
Calendar Years 1998–1999
(Costs in Millions of Dollars)

Type and Model	Number		Flyaway Cost[b]		Weapon System Cost[c]	
	1998	1999	1998	1999	1998	1999
NAVY—TOTAL	72	42	$1,518[r]	$1,563	$1,821[r]	$1,839
Patrol—TOTAL	3	6	$ 198[r]	$ 415	$ 213[r]	$ 436
E-2	3	6	198[r]	415	213[r]	436
Fighter/Attack—TOTAL	25	18	843	481	968	638
F/A-18	15	8	603	257	653	340
AV-8B	10	10	239	224	315	298
Transports/Tankers—TOTAL	—	5	—	421	—	436
UC-35	—	2	—	9	—	10
V-22	—	3	—	412	—	426
Trainers—TOTAL	33	12	319	216	456	293
T-39	17	—	27	—	43	—
T-45A	16	12	292	216	413	293
Helicopters—TOTAL............	11	1	159	31	184	36
AH-1W	8	—	75	—	92	—
CH-53	3	1	84	31	92	36

Source: Department of the Navy.
   a Navy acceptances for own use; excludes FMS shipments.
   b Flyaway Cost includes airframe, engines, electronics, communications, armament, other installed equipment, non-recurring costs, and ancillary equipment.
   c Weapons System Cost (Investment Cost) includes flyaway cost, initial spares, ground equipment, training equipment, and other support items.
   r Revised.

MILITARY AIRCRAFT ACCEPTANCES
FOR REIMBURSABLE PROGRAMS[a]
Calendar Years 1998–1999
(Millions of Dollars)

Accepting Agency, Type, and Model	Number of Aircraft Accepted		Flyaway Cost [b]	
	1998	1999	1998	1999
TOTAL ACCEPTANCES FOR REIMBURSABLE PROGRAMS ...	175 [r]	114	$5,803 [r]	$3,527
AIR FORCE—TOTAL	149	90	$4,290 [r]	$2,832
Fighter/Attack—TOTAL	149	90	4,920 [r]	2,832
F-15	41	23	2,723 [r]	1,528
F-16	108	67	2,197 [r]	1,304
NAVY—TOTAL	22 [r]	24	$ 783 [r]	$ 694
Patrol—TOTAL	2	—	132	—
E-2C	2	—	132	—
Fighter/Attack—TOTAL	13	17	458	599
F/A-18	13	17	458 [E]	599 [E]
Helicopters—TOTAL...............	7 [r]	7	193	96
AH-1	—	7	—	96
SH-2	7 [r]	—	193 [E]	—
ARMY—TOTAL	4	—	$ 100	$ —
Helicopters—TOTAL...............	4	—	100	$ —
AH-64	4	—	100 [E]	—

Source: Aerospace Industries Association, based on USAF, USN, and USA survey responses.
   a   Foreign government aircraft purchases through the Department of Defense Foreign Military Sales program.
   b   Flyaway cost includes airframes, engines, electronics, communications, armament, other installed equipment, and non-recurring costs associated with the manufacture of the aircraft.
   E   Estimate.
   r   Revised.

MILITARY AIRCRAFT PROGRAM PROCUREMENT
Fiscal Years 1999, 2000, and 2001
(Millions of Dollars[a])

Agency and Model	1999		2000 [E]		2001 [E]	
	No.	Cost	No.	Cost	No.	Cost
AIR FORCE						
B-2 Spirit............................	—	$ 243.4	—	$ 112.3	—	$ 61.3
C-17 Globemaster III............	13	2,873.0	15	3,354.9	12	2,890.9
C-32 A/B	2	158.9	1	73.0	—	—
C-130J Hercules[b]	7	497.8	2	210.1	4	362.9
Civil Air Patrol Aircraft	27	3.0	27	2.5	27	2.5
E-8C JSTARS	2	508.9	1	287.6	1	260.6
F-15E Eagle	—	—	5	291.6	—	—
F-16 Falcon........................	1	36.2	10	262.2	—	—
F-22 Raptor	2	770.0	—	280.5	10	2,546.1
JPATS[b]............................	22	108.2	41	166.9	41	188.2
Operational Support Aircraft	—	—	1	61.8	—	—
Unmanned Aerial Vehicles ...	7	129.8	7	57.1	7	44.5
VCX	4	159.8	—	—	—	—
ARMY						
AH-64 Apache	—	$ 616.4	—	$ 781.4	—	$ 744.5
C-XX................................	5	26.8	1	5.3	—	—
UH-60 Black Hawk	29	269.8	19	215.9	6	86.8
NAVY						
AV-8B Harrier.....................	11	$ 331.7	11	$ 300.5	10	$ 226.6
C-40A	—	—	1	48.7	—	—
CH-60S	5	135.3	17	357.5	15	245.5
E-2C Hawkeye	3	395.8	3	382.6	5	320.9
EA-6B Prowler	—	208.9	—	264.5	—	203.1
F/A-18E/F Hornet	30	2,816.4	36	2,837.8	42	2,919.6
SH-60R	—	—	7	216.7	4	162.3
T-45 Goshawk	15	300.6	15	332.9	12	273.7
UC-35	—	—	2	11.9	—	—
V-22 Osprey[b]	7	679.4	11	963.6	16	1,571.4
VP-3	—	—	—	—	1	50.3

Source: Department of Defense Budget, "Program Acquisition Costs by Weapon System" (Annually) and "Procurement Programs (P-1)" (Annually).
NOTE: See Research and Development Chapter for aircraft program RDT&E authorization data.
  a Total Obligational Authority for procurement, excluding initial spares.
  b Air Force and Navy funding.
  E Estimate. Latest year reflects Administration's budget proposal.

ACTIVE U.S. MILITARY AIRCRAFT[a]
Fiscal Years 1980–1999

Year	Total[a]	Fixed-Wing Aircraft				Helicopters
		Total	Jet	Turboprop	Piston	
1980	18,969	11,362	8,794	1,869	699	7,607
1981	19,363	11,645	9,111	1,943	591	7,718
1982	21,728	12,063	9,647	1,900	516	9,665
1983	18,652	11,603	9,495	1,745	363	7,049
1984	18,833	11,661	9,551	1,777	333	7,172
1985	19,333	11,929	9,640	1,881	408	7,404
1986	20,157	11,919	9,730	1,803	386	8,238
1987	20,514	12,054	9,819	1,865	370	8,460
1988	21,010	12,481	9,954	2,222	305	8,529
1989	19,223	11,893	9,501	2,131	261	7,330
1990	20,017	12,817	10,360	2,199	258	7,200
1991	19,966	12,587	10,221	2,119	247	7,379
1992	19,210	11,936	9,672	2,035	229	7,274
1993	17,231	9,681	7,651	1,852	178	7,550
1994 [E]	17,018	9,803	7,786	1,835	182	7,215
1995 [E]	16,207	9,277	7,294	1,754	229	6,930
1996 [b]	20,554	10,154	7,798	2,199	157	10,400
1997	20,245	9,677	7,364	2,151	162	10,568
1998	15,585	9,187 [c]	7,082	1,951	120	6,398
1999	16,062	9,015 [d]	6,981	1,908	115	7,047

Source: Aerospace Industries Association.
a   Includes Army, Air Force, Navy, and Marine regular service aircraft, as well as Reserve and National Guard Aircraft.
b   Prior years data provided by Office of the Secretary of Defense and limited to aircraft in the continental United States.
E   Estimate.
c   Includes 34 gliders.
d   Includes 11 gliders.

DEPARTMENT OF DEFENSE
OUTLAYS FOR AIRCRAFT PROCUREMENT
By Agency
Fiscal Years 1966–2001
(Millions of Dollars)

Year	TOTAL AIRCRAFT PROCUREMENT	Air Force	Navy	Army
1966	$ 6,635	$ 4,074	$ 2,021	$ 540
1967	8,411	4,842	2,607	962
1968	9,462	5,079	3,244	1,139
1969	9,177	5,230	2,821	1,126
1970	7,948	4,623	2,488	837
1971	6,631	3,960	2,125	546
1972	5,927	3,191	2,347	389
1973	5,066	2,396	2,557	113
1974	5,006	2,078	2,806	122
1975	5,484	2,211	3,137	136
1976	6,520	3,323	3,061	136
Tr.Qtr.	1,557	859	672	26
1977	6,608	3,586	2,721	301
1978	6,971	3,989	2,602	380
1979	8,836	5,138	3,140	558
1980	11,124	6,647	3,689	787
1981	13,193	7,941	4,397	855
1982	16,793	9,624	5,872	1,297
1983	21,013	11,799	7,490	1,724
1984	23,196	12,992	8,040	2,165
1985	26,586	15,619	8,263	2,705
1986	30,828	18,919	8,922	2,987
1987	32,956	20,036	9,614	3,306
1988	28,246	15,961	9,407	2,878
1989	27,569	14,662	10,073	2,834
1990	26,142	14,303	9,031	2,808
1991	25,689	13,794	9,055	2,840
1992	23,581	13,154	7,907	2,520
1993	20,359	11,438	7,246	1,675
1994	18,840	10,303	6,826	1,711
1995	16,125	8,891	5,685	1,549
1996	14,331	7,862	5,034	1,435
1997	14,663	7,799	5,322	1,542
1998	15,473	8,236	5,845	1,392
1999	16,484	8,928	6,024	1,532
2000 [E]	15,666	7,066	7,210	1,390
2001 [E]	17,100	8,312	7,479	1,309

Source: Office of Management and Budget, "Budget of the United States Government" (Annually).
NOTE: Detail may not add to totals because of rounding.
  E Estimate. Latest year reflects Administration's budget proposal.
Tr.Qtr. See Glossary.

SPECIFICATIONS OF U.S. MILITARY AIRCRAFT
On Order or in Production as of 1999

Primary Mission, DoD Designation, & Popular Name	Manufacturer	U.S. Military Service	Crew	Empty Weight (000's lbs)	Engines	Performance Typical for Primary Mission	Remarks
ATTACK							
AV-8B Harrier II	Boeing/BAe	USMC	1	14	1xRR F402	Mach 1.0	V/STOL
FIGHTERS							
F-15E Eagle	Boeing	USAF	2	37	2xP&W F100	Mach 2.5 class	Dual role fighter/long range interdiction
F-16A/B Fighting Falcon	LM	USAF	1-2	17	1xP&W F100	Mach 2+ class	Multirole fighter; fully fly-by-wire; missiles, guns.
F-16C/D Fighting Falcon	LM	USAF	1-2	19	1xP&W F100/ 1xGE F110	Mach 2+ class	Provisions for AMRAAM, LANTIRN, Harpoon, HARM
F/A-18C/D Hornet	Boeing/NGC	USN/USMC	1-2	23	2xGE F404	Mach 1.8 class	Multi-mission strike fighter
F/A-18E/F Hornet	Boeing/NGC	USN/USMC	1-2	31	2xGE F414	Mach 1.8 class	Multi-mission strike fighter
F-22A Raptor	LM/Boeing	USAF	1	NA	2xPW F119	Mach 2+ class	Air superiority with near-precision ground attack
COMMAND/CONTROL AND PATROL							
E-2C Hawkeye	NGC	USN	5	40	2xRR T56	6+ hr. mission duration	AEW command & control; active & passive detection
E-8C Joint STARS	NGC	USAF/Army	21+	171	4xP&W JT3D	11-20+ hr. loiter	Ground surveillance/battle mgmt
RC-12 P/Q	Raytheon	Army	2	9	2xP&W PT6A	4 hr. loiter	Electronic intercept
CARGO-TRANSPORT							
C-12R	Raytheon	Army	2	8	2xP&W PT6A	268 mph; 788 n.m.	Utility/transport
C-17A Globemaster III	Boeing	USAF	3	277	4xP&W F117	Mach 0.77; 2,400 n.m.	102 troops or 170,000 lbs.
C-20F/G/H	Gulfstream	All	2	42-43	2xRR Tay	Mach 0.80; 4,200 n.m.	Versions of Gulfstream IV
C-32A	Boeing	USAF	16	132	2xP&W 2040	Mach 0.80; 4,150 n.m.	Executive personnel transport
C-37A	Gulfstream	USAF/Army	2	48	2xBR 710	Mach 0.80; 6,500 n.m.	Version of Gulfstream V
C-40A	Boeing	USN	3-7	92	2xCFM 56-7	Mach 0.79; 3,000 n.m.	Navy Unique Fleet Essential Aircraft
C/EC/WC-130J	LM	USAF/ANG	3	97	4xRR AE2100	396 mph; 3,260 mi.	41,000 lbs.
KC-130J	LM	USMC	3	97	4xRR AE2100	12,100 gals.	Tanker
CV/MV-22 Osprey	Bell/Boeing	USMC/USAF	3-4	33	2xRR T406	Max 316 mph; 2,200 n.m.	With internal fuel tanks, engines tilt for VTOL
TRAINING							
T-1A Jayhawk	Raytheon	USAF	2	10	2xP&W JT-15D	Max 538 mph	Tanker/transport trainer
T-6A Texan II	Raytheon	USN/USAF	2	5	1xP&W PT6A	Max 368 mph	Primary trainer
T-45C Goshawk	Boeing/BAe	USN	2	9	1xRR F405	Mach 1.04 at 25,000 ft.	Next generation trainer
TH-67 Creek	Bell	Army	1	2	1xRR 250	Max 135 mph; 405 mi.	Rotary wing trainer
HELICOPTERS							
AH-64D Apache	Boeing	Army	2	11	2xGE T700	Max 197 mph; 445 mi.	Attack helicopter
CH-47SD	Boeing	Army	3	25	2xRR T55	Max 178 mph; 750 mi.	Heavy-lift helicopter
CH-53E	Sikorsky	USN	3-8	33-36	3xGE T64	Max 196 mph; 710 mi.	55 passengers, aux. tanks/ minesweeping
CH-60	Sikorsky	USN	4	11	2xGE T700	Max 184 mph; 373 mi.	Vertical replenishment
HH/SH-60 Seahawk	Sikorsky	USN	4-12	14	2xGE T700	Max 184 mph; 500 mi.	Combat search and rescue, SOF
HH/MH-60G Pave Hawk	Sikorsky	USAF	3	12	2xGE T700	Max 184 mph; 1,380 mi.	11 troops; combat; search; rescue
RAH-66 Comanche	Boeing/Sikorsky	Army	2	9	2xLHTEC T800	Max 201 mph; 1,450 mi.	Armed recon./light attack
SH-2G Super Sea-Sprite	Kaman	USN	3-4	9	2xGE T700	Max 159 mph; 500 mi.	Multi-mission helicopter
UH-60L Black Hawk	Sikorsky	Army	3	11	2xGE T700	Max 184 mph; 373 mi.	Utility assault helicopter

Source: Aerospace Industries Association, based on company reports.
KEY: BAe = British Aerospace; BR = BMW-Rolls Royce; GE = General Electric; LHTEC = Light Helicopter Turbine Engine Co.; LM = Lockheed Martin; NGC = Northrop Grumman; P&W = Pratt & Whitney; RR = Rolls Royce.
NA Not available.

SALES OF MISSILE SYSTEMS AND PARTS ROSE FOR A SECOND straight year in 1999 to $4.5 billion, up from $4.4 billion for 1998, according to revised Bureau of the Census figures. On the other hand, net new orders for missile systems and parts fell 14% from $4.9 billion to $4.2 billion in 1999. As a result, the unfilled order backlog fell $0.7 billion to end 1999 at $5.8 billion.

DoD outlays for missile procurement declined for the ninth straight year in FY 1999. DoD expenditures fell 17% to $4.1 billion, with the Air Force accounting for $2.3 billion, Navy $998 million, and Army $783 million. Missile procurement will rise to $4.3 billion in FY 2000 and $4.5 billion in FY 2001 in OMB's estimation.

According to the DoD's "Program Acquisition Costs by Weapon System" report, missile programs in production in 1999/2000, and scheduled to receive continued funding in FY 2001 include:

Air Force: Joint Direct Attack Munition (JDAM), a USAF/USN program, $244.2 million; Advanced Medium Range Air-to-Air Missile (AMRAAM), another USAF/USN program, $137.6 million; Sensor Fuzed Weapon (SFW), $107.2 million; and Wind-Corrected Munitions Dispenser (WCMD), $104.0 million.

Navy: Trident II, $462.7 million; Joint Standoff Weapon (JSOW), a USN/USAF program, $262.4 million; Standard air defense missile, $170.4 million; Standoff Land Attack Missile-Extended Range (SLAM-ER),

$27.9 million; and Rolling Airframe Missile (RAM), $23.1 million.

Army: Javelin advanced antitank weapon, an Army/USMC program, $401.3 million; Hellfire helicopter-launched antiarmor missile, $285.4 million; Army Tactical Missile System (ATACMS), $245.3 million; Brilliant Antiarmor Submunition (BAT), $134.9 million; and Avenger mobile antiaircraft weapon system, $29.9 million.

BMDO: Patriot, a BMDO/Army program, $365.5 million.

Ballistic Missile Defense was the single greatest recipient of DoD missile RDT&E funding. "Program Acquisition Costs by Weapon System" reported that RDT&E funding for Ballistic Missile Defense totaled $3.3 billion in FY 1999 and is projected to rise to $4.3 billion in FY 2000 before dropping back to $3.9 billion in FY 2001. The next largest missile research programs in FY 2001 will be the Joint Air-to-Surface Standoff Missile (JASSM) led by the Air Force, at $122.3 million; Army's BAT, at $96.1 million; and Navy's Tomahawk, at $91.4 million.

MISSILE PROGRAM PROCUREMENT
Fiscal Years 1999, 2000, and 2001
(Millions of Dollars[a])

Agency and Model	1999		2000 [E]		2001 [E]	
	No.	Cost	No.	Cost	No.	Cost
AIR FORCE						
AMRAAM[b]	280	$140.2	287	$135.8	279	$137.6
JDAM[b]	4,523	137.1	10,022	270.9	9,770	244.2
SFW	386	118.0	214	85.4	300	107.2
WCMD	676	14.9	2,990	48.6	6,308	104.0
NAVY						
AIM-9X[b]	—	$ —	—	$ —	155	$ 55.9
JSOW[b]	414	165.9	528	155.2	810	262.4
RAM........................	95	44.3	90	45.3	—	23.1
SLAM-ER	102	61.6	20	24.7	30	27.9
SRAW	—	—	—	—	698	43.4
Standard	114	212.7	86	198.1	96	170.4
Tomahawk	624	439.2	—	—	—	—
Trident II	5	310.3	12	487.1	12	462.7
ARMY						
ATACMS	120	$240.3	158	$318.8	55	$245.3
Avenger	15	34.7	15	34.2	7	29.9
BAT	304	94.5	609	142.9	741	134.9
Hellfire....................	2,000	343.3	2,200	292.9	2,200	285.4
Javelin[c]	4,310	420.5	3,523	437.3	4,047	401.3
MLRS	—	—	—	3.7	—	9.4
SADARM.................	30	31.3	—	14.9	—	14.9
BMDO						
Patriot[d].....................	—	$187.4	32	$343.8	40	$365.5
TMD BMC3	—	22.5	—	—	—	3.9
Navy Area Theater[f] ...	—	42.7	7	18.1	—	—
NMD	—	—	—	—	—	74.5

Source: Department of Defense, "Program Acquisition Costs by Weapon System" (Annually).
NOTE: See Research and Development Chapter for missile program RDT&E authorization data.
  a Total Obligational Authority excluding initial spares and RDT&E.
  b Navy and Air Force funding.
  c Army and Marine Corps funding.
  d Army and BMDO funding.
  E Estimate. Latest year reflects Administration's budget proposal.
  f Navy and BMDO funding.
NA Not available.

DEPARTMENT OF DEFENSE
OUTLAYS FOR MISSILE PROCUREMENT

By Agency
Fiscal Years 1966–2001
(Millions of Dollars)

Year	TOTAL MISSILE PROCUREMENT	Air Force	Navy	Army
1966	$ 2,069	$1,313	$ 512	$ 244
1967	1,930	1,278	432	220
1968	2,219	1,388	436	395
1969	2,509	1,382	534	593
1970	2,912	1,467	702	743
1971	3,140	1,497	791	852
1972	3,009	1,334	831	844
1973	3,023	1,454	628	941
1974	2,981	1,537	541	903
1975	2,889	1,602	615	672
1976	2,296	1,549	584	163
Tr.Qtr.	402	347	148	(93)
1977	2,781	1,501	905	374
1978	3,096 [a]	1,376	1,302 [a]	418
1979	3,786	1,537	1,702	547
1980	4,434	1,810	1,973	651
1981	5,809	2,366	2,297	1,146
1982	6,782	3,069	2,444	1,269
1983	7,795	3,383	2,812	1,600
1984	9,527	4,640	2,809	2,079
1985	10,749	5,409	2,941	2,399
1986	11,731	6,473	2,780	2,478
1987	11,473	6,002	3,157	2,314
1988	11,676	6,046	3,392	2,239
1989	14,503	7,349	4,445	2,709
1990	14,851	7,951	4,446	2,453
1991	14,400	6,906	4,954	2,540
1992	13,504	6,409	4,694	2,401
1993	11,404	5,424	3,794	2,187
1994	8,934	4,312	3,238	1,384
1995	7,513	3,845	2,694	974
1996	6,199	3,235	2,045	919
1997	5,225	2,743	1,546	936
1998	4,907	2,543	1,400	964
1999	4,080	2,299	998	783
2000 [E]	4,289	2,191	1,040	1,058
2001 [E]	4,489	2,290	1,058	1,141

Source: Office of Management and Budget, "The Budget of the United States Government" (Annually).
NOTE: Detail may not add to totals because of rounding.
   a   Beginning 1978, DoD combined Navy Missile Procurement with torpedoes and other related products into Navy Weapons Procurement. Missiles comprise approximately 80 percent of the value of this category.
   E   Estimate. Latest year reflects Administration's budget proposal.
Tr.Qtr.   See Glossary.

MAJOR MISSILE PROGRAMS
RESEARCH, DEVELOPMENT, PRODUCTION

Program	Agency	Status	Systems Contractor	Propulsion Manufacturer	Guidance Manufacturer
AIR-TO-AIR					
AMRAAM-120B/C	USAF/USN	P	Raytheon	Alliant/ARC/ Aerojet	Raytheon/ Litton
Sidewinder-9M	USN/USAF	P	NASC	Alliant	Raytheon
Sidewinder-9X	USN/USAF	D	Raytheon	Alliant	Raytheon
AIR-TO-SURFACE					
AGM-130A/B	USAF	P	Boeing	Alliant	Boeing/HI
AGM-142	USAF	P	LM/Rafael	Rafael	Litton/BAe
AGM-86B/C	USAF	P	Boeing	WI	Litton/Boeing/ Interstate
GATS/GAM	USAF	P	NGC	—	Honeywell
GBU-15	USAF	P	Boeing	—	Boeing
HARM-88A/B	USN/USAF	P	Raytheon	TKC	Raytheon
*Harpoon-84A/C/D	USN	P	Boeing	TCM/TKC	Ray/Kearfott/ IBM/LSI
*Harpoon-84E	USN	P	Boeing	TCM/TKC	HI
JASSM	USN/USAF	D	LM	TCM	HI/Litton
JDAM	USAF/USN	D	Boeing	—	HI/Boeing
JSOW-154	USN/USAF	D	Raytheon	—	Kearfott
Maverick-65D/G/H/K	USAF	P	Raytheon	Alliant	Raytheon
Maverick-65F	USN	P	Raytheon	Alliant	Raytheon
Maverick-65J	USN/USMC	D	Raytheon	Alliant	Raytheon
Paveway-Enhanced	USN/USAF	P	Raytheon	—	Raytheon/BAe
SLAM-84E	USN	P	Boeing	TCM	Boeing/Ray/HI
WCMD	USAF	P	LM	—	LM/HI/BAe

* Also Surface-to-Surface

(Continued on next page)

MAJOR MISSILE PROGRAMS
(Continued)

Program	Agency	Status	Systems Contractor	Propulsion Manufacturer	Guidance Manufacturer
ANTI-SUBMARINE					
VLA-44A	USN	P	LM	TKC	LM
SURFACE-TO-AIR					
Hawk-23B	Army	P	Raytheon	Aerojet/ARC	Raytheon
MEADS	Army	D	LM	—	LM
NMD	Army	R,D	Boeing	Alliant/UTC	Boeing
Patriot-104	Army	P	Raytheon	ARC/Aerojet	Raytheon
PAC-3	Army	P	LM	ARC	LM/HI/ Boeing
RAM-116A	USN	P	Raytheon	ARC	Raytheon
RAM-116B	USN	D	Raytheon	ARC/Alliant	Raytheon
SeaSparrow-7M	USN	P	Raytheon	Alliant	Raytheon
SeaSparrow- Evolved	USN	D	Raytheon	Alliant/Raufoss	Raytheon/HI
SLID	Army	D	Boeing	ARC	Boeing
Standard 2 MR	USN	P	Raytheon	ARC	HI/Raytheon
Standard 2 ER	USN	P	Raytheon	ARC	HI/Raytheon
Standard 2-IV	USN	P	Raytheon	ARC/UTC	HI/Raytheon
Standard 2-IVA	USN	D	Raytheon	ARC/UTC	HI/Raytheon
Standard 3	USN	D	Raytheon	TKC	—
Stinger-92D/E	All	P	Raytheon	ARC	Raytheon
THAAD	Army	D	LM	UTC/Boeing	—

(Continued on next page)

MAJOR MISSILE PROGRAMS
(Continued)

Program	Agency	Status	Systems Contractor	Propulsion Manufacturer	Guidance Manufacturer
SURFACE-TO-SURFACE					
*Harpoon-84A/C/D	USN	P	Boeing	TCM/TKC	Ray/IBM/LSI/ NGC/Kearfott
*Harpoon-84E	USN	P	Boeing	TCM/TKC	HI
Minuteman III	USAF	P	TRW	TKC/UTC	Boeing
Tomahawk (SLCM)	USN	P	Raytheon	WI/UTC/ARC	Ray/Litton
Tomahawk Tactical	USN	D	Raytheon	WI/ARC	Ray/HI
Trident 2 (D-5)	USN	P	LM	Alliant/TKC/ ARC	LM/Draper/ Ray/Boeing/ Kearfott
BATTLEFIELD SUPPORT AND ANTIARMOR					
ATACMS	Army	P	LM	ARC	Honeywell
BAT	Army	P	NGC	—	NGC/Ray/BAe
Dragon-47	Army	P	Boeing	Boeing/Alliant	Boeing
GMLRS	Army	D	LM	ARC	Litton/HI
HELLFIRE II-114K	Army/USMC	P	LM	Alliant	LM
Longbow HELLFIRE 114L	Army/USMC	P	LM/NGC	Alliant	LM/NGC/BAe
LOSAT	Army	D	LM	Alliant	Ray/HI
Javelin	Army/USMC	P	Ray/LM	ARC	LM/Ray/BAe
MLRS-26,-270A1	Army	P	LM	ARC	—
MPIM/SRAW	Army	D	LM	Alliant	LM
Predator	USMC	D	LM	Alliant	LM
SMAW	USMC	P	Boeing	Boeing	—
TOW2A-71E	Army	P	Raytheon	Alliant	Raytheon
TOW2B-71F	Army	P	Raytheon	Alliant	Raytheon

Source: Aerospace Industries Association, based on company reports.
Status: R-Research; D-Development; P-Production.
  * Also Air-to-Surface

Abb:	ARC	— Atlantic Research	LM	— Lockheed Martin	TCM	— Teledyne Continental Motors
	BAe	— BAe Systems	NASC	— Naval Air Systems Command	TKC	— Thiokol Propulsion
	HI	— Honeywell	NGC	— Northrop Grumman	UTC	— United Technologies
	LSI	— Lear Siegler	Ray	— Raytheon	WI	— Williams International

ORDERS, SALES, AND BACKLOG
MISSILE SYSTEMS AND PARTS[a]
Calendar Years 1985–1999
(Millions of Dollars)

Year	SALES—Current Dollars	SALES—Constant Dollars[br]
1985	$ 7,975	$ 8,080
1986	8,236	8,253
1987	9,671	9,671
1988	9,485	9,345
1989	9,283	8,799
1990	9,102	8,381
1991	8,989	8,069
1992	9,032	7,726
1993	7,713	6,417
1994	5,294	4,315
1995	4,688	3,765
1996	4,792	3,782
1997	4,024	3,149
1998[r]	4,356	3,395
1999	4,521	3,494

Year	NET NEW ORDERS	BACKLOG AS OF DECEMBER 31
1985	$ 8,122	$10,190
1986	11,023	12,754
1987	11,482	14,302
1988	9,437	14,255
1989	8,998	14,005
1990	7,917	12,956
1991	8,072	12,571
1992	9,234	11,814
1993	4,775	9,305
1994	2,785	5,823
1995	3,164	4,833
1996	8,672	6,563
1997	4,239	5,828
1998[r]	4,884	6,539
1999	4,204	5,792

Source: Bureau of the Census, "Aerospace Industry (Orders, Sales, and Backlog)" Series MA37D (Annually).
a Excludes engines and propulsion units where separable.
b Based on AIA's aerospace composite price deflator, 1987=100.
r Revised.

BALLISTIC MISSILE DEFENSE ORGANIZATION
FUNDING BY PROJECT NUMBER
Fiscal Years 1996–2000
(Millions of Dollars)

Project Number and Title		1996	1997	1998	1999	2000 [E]
1151	Sensors	$192	$ —	$ —	$ —	$ —
1155	Discrimination.................................	58	68	83	19	28
1161	Advanced Sensor Technology	19	35	29	17	4
1170	TMD Risk Reduction	42	23	31	26	—
1184	Engineering Analysis	—	—	—	14	13
1262	Mead Concepts	20	59	50	12	49
1264	Atmospheric Interceptor.....................	—	—	32	—	—
1266	Navy Theater Wide Defense...............	200	304	438	366	369
1267	Ground-Based Interceptor	287	—	—	—	—
1270	Advanced Interceptors	36	70	43	—	—
1281	Atmospheric Interceptor Technology ...	—	—	—	44	40
1282	Exoatmospheric Interceptor Technology	—	—	—	30	19
1294	BPI/TMD Concept Development	6	24	14	6	5
1360	Directed Energy Programs	76	94	118	121	70
1460	BM/C3 Technologies	81	—	—	—	—
1461	BMC4I	—	—	—	19	16
1651	Innovative Science & Technology	47	59	57	23	14
1660	Statutory & Mandated Programs	53	68	61	63	64
2160	TMD Existing System Modifications......	20	16	10	2	—
2257	PATRIOT	662	602	559	429	525
2259	ACES/ADP	59	42	95	46	80
2260	THAAD..	520	616	387	432	588
2263	Navy Area TBMD	298	309	307	285	318

(Continued on next page)

BALLISTIC MISSILE DEFENSE ORGANIZATION
FUNDING BY PROJECT NUMBER (Continued)
Fiscal Years 1996–2000
(Millions of Dollars)

Project Number and Title		1996	1997	1998	1999	2000 [E]
2358	HAWK System BM/C3	$ 37	$ 15	$ —	$ —	$ —
2401	NMD Integration	—	24	200	1,186	466
2402	Sensor Technology	—	54	18	10	6
2403	Ground-Based Interceptor	—	272	267	139	31
2404	BM/C3 Ground-Based Radar	—	51	61	22	26
2405	Ground-Based Radar	—	66	58	35	29
2406	UEWR	—	12	10	6	10
2407	Systems Engineering	—	47	26	29	29
2408	Deployment Planning	—	12	15	33	45
2409	Program Support	—	28	54	68	95
2410	Test & Evaluation	—	103	130	116	154
3152	NMD System Engineering	55	—	—	—	—
3153	Systems Architecture & Engineering	13	11	19	18	16
3155	TAMD Integration	—	—	—	19	108
3157	Environment, Siting, & Facilities	10	6	5	—	—
3160	Deployment Planning	23	2	—	—	—
3251	System Engineering & Technical Support	44	46	48	33	—
3261	TMD BM/C3I	65	48	83	56	48
3265	Joint TMD Warfighter Support	18	16	14	15	—
3270	Threat & Countermeasures	28	28	30	26	22
3352	Modeling & Simulation	87	104	77	63	38
3353	Joint National Test Facility	—	—	48	57	53
3354	Targets Support	23	22	69	20	61
3359	System Test & Evaluation	63	39	39	24	42
3360	Test Resources	42	49	75	91	82
4000	Management	157	143	140	123	133
	Other programs[a]	—	35	—	19	17
	TOTAL DETAILED PROJECTS	$3,343	$3,622	$3,800	$4,173	$3,783

Source: Ballistic Missile Defense Organization.
a Projects with five year funding under $20 million herein combined.
E Estimate. Represents Administration's budget request.

ALES OF SPACE VEHICLE SYSTEMS DECLINED IN 1999 FROM $9.5 billion to $9 billion, according to revised figures compiled by the U.S. Census Bureau. Where separable, figures for space vehicle systems exclude engines and propulsion units, which are reported below. Non-military (civil) sales fell 26% to $3.9 billion in 1999. However, sales of military space vehicle systems rose 21% to $5.1 billion.

Orders for space vehicle systems fell 25% to $9.3 billion. Civil orders declined 74% to $2.1 billion—their lowest level since 1986. Military orders, on the other hand, helped offset part of the decline—rising 60% to $7.3 billion in 1999.

As a result, the backlog of unfilled orders for space vehicle systems rose $653 million to $21 billion by the end of 1999. This compares with $20.4 billion in 1998. While the civil backlog, at $11 billion, declined for the second straight year, the military backlog grew to a record $10 billion.

Sales of engines and propulsion units for missiles and space vehicles declined 6.4% to $2.1 billion in 1999. Civil sales—representing 76% of the total—fell 9.3% to $1.6 billion. Military sales, on the other hand, rose $20 million to $516 million.

Both civil and military orders for engines and propulsion units rose in 1999. Combined net new orders more than doubled in 1999 to $4.9 billion. While civil orders contrib-uted the majority of that increase, military orders rose $17 million to $672 million.

Consequently, the unfilled order backlog rose 45% to $6.2 billion. The civil backlog rose 64%, or $2 billion, while military orders on backlog declined $94 million to $1.0 billion.

Federal funding for space activities in FY 1999 declined slightly to an estimated $26 billion, according to NASA's annual "Aeronautics and Space Report of the President." The two largest recipients were DoD with $12.5 billion (up from $12.2 billion) and NASA with $12.4 billion (down from $12.9 billion in FY 1998). Space outlays at the Department of Commerce rose from $326 million in FY 1998 to $431 million in FY 1999. Other federal spending, including Energy Department funding, grew $27 million (8.2%) to $358 million.

Total NASA outlays in FY 1999 declined $542 million to $13.7 billion. While nearly all budget categories registered declines, "Science, Aeronautics, and Technology" fell the most—down $230 million. "Science, Aeronautics, and Technology" spending declined further in FY 2000—down another $419 million to $5.4 billion. As a result, total NASA outlays fell in FY 2000—down $236 million to $13.4 billion.

Procurement funding for selected DoD space programs, as detailed in "Program Acquisition Costs by Weapon System," totaled $991 million in FY 1999 and was projected to fall 12% in FY 2000. The largest reported expenditure in FY 1999 ($536 million) went to the Air Force's Titan launch vehicle, whose projected funding declined in FY 2000 to $429 million.

RDT&E funding for these same programs fell $120 million from $1.7 billion in FY 1999 to $1.6 billion in FY 2000, but is projected to rise to $1.8 billion in FY 2001. The Space-Based Infrared System (SBIRS), at $646 million, received the largest reported funding in FY 2000. Other major development programs were Milstar, $357 million, and the Evolved Expendable Launch Vehicle (EELV), $318 million. The EELV is scheduled to receive initial production funding of $68 million in FY 2000.

ORDERS, SALES, AND BACKLOG
SPACE VEHICLE SYSTEMS[a]
Calendar Years 1985–1999
(Millions of Dollars)

Year	SALES—Current Dollars			SALES—Constant Dollars[br]		
	TOTAL	Military	Non-Military	TOTAL	Military	Non-Military
1985	$ 6,300	$4,241	$ 2,059	$ 6,383	$ 4,297	$ 2,086
1986	6,304	4,579	1,725	6,317	4,588	1,728
1987	8,051	5,248	2,803	8,051	5,248	2,803
1988	8,622	6,190	2,432	8,495	6,099	2,396
1989	9,758	6,457	3,301	9,249	6,120	3,129
1990	9,691	6,556	3,135	8,924	6,037	2,887
1991	10,515	6,770	3,745	9,439	6,077	3,362
1992	9,266	5,887	3,379	7,926	5,036	2,891
1993	7,317	4,175	3,142	6,087	3,473	2,614
1994	10,594	5,707	4,887	8,634	4,651	3,983
1995	11,314	4,782	6,532	9,088	3,841	5,247
1996	11,698	5,613	6,085	9,233	4,430	4,803
1997	14,643	4,919	9,724	11,458	3,849	7,609
1998[r]	9,491	4,227	5,264	7,398	3,295	4,103
1999	9,022	5,107	3,915	6,972	3,947	3,026

Year	NET NEW ORDERS			BACKLOG AS OF DECEMBER 31		
	TOTAL	Military	Non-Military	TOTAL	Military	Non-Military
1985	$ 8,383	$6,083	$ 2,300	$ 6,707	$ 4,941	$ 1,766
1986	7,437	5,666	1,771	8,063	6,028	2,035
1987	11,455	9,000	2,455	12,393	9,460	2,933
1988	7,296	4,561	2,735	10,838	7,880	2,958
1989	11,709	8,107	3,602	13,356	9,192	4,164
1990	9,598	6,256	3,342	12,462	8,130	4,332
1991	11,222	5,468	5,754	11,664	6,221	5,443
1992	10,491	6,773	3,718	12,809	7,622	5,187
1993	8,436	5,106	3,330	13,663	7,384	6,279
1994	9,041	4,896	4,145	12,888	6,732	6,156
1995	13,212	4,679	8,533	15,650	5,872	9,778
1996	16,527	8,888	7,639	23,004	9,125	13,879
1997	15,078	4,584	10,494	23,189	8,848	14,341
1998[r]	12,420	4,563	7,857	20,372	7,970	12,402
1999	9,340	7,283	2,057	21,025	10,036	10,989

Source: Bureau of the Census, "Aerospace Industry (Orders, Sales, and Backlog)" Series MA37D (Annually).
a Excludes engines and propulsion units where separable.
b Based on AIA's aerospace composite price deflator, 1987=100.
r Revised.

ORDERS, SALES, AND BACKLOG
ENGINES AND PROPULSION UNITS FOR
MISSILES AND SPACE VEHICLES
Calendar Years 1985–1999
(Millions of Dollars)

Year	SALES—Current Dollars			SALES—Constant Dollars[ar]		
	TOTAL	Military	Non-Military	TOTAL	Military	Non-Military
1985	$2,466	$1,256	$1,210	$2,498	$1,273	$1,226
1986	2,995	1,796	1,199	3,001	1,800	1,201
1987	2,993	1,563	1,430	2,993	1,563	1,430
1988	3,407	1,830	1,577	3,357	1,803	1,554
1989	3,602	1,771	1,831	3,414	1,679	1,736
1990	3,247	1,911	1,336	2,990	1,760	1,230
1991	3,807	1,869	1,938	3,417	1,678	1,740
1992	3,051	1,577	1,474	2,610	1,349	1,261
1993	3,104	1,619	1,485	2,582	1,347	1,235
1994	2,518	1,123	1,395	2,052	915	1,137
1995	2,364	1,035	1,329	1,899	831	1,067
1996	2,016	635	1,381	1,591	501	1,090
1997	2,687	558	2,129	2,103	437	1,666
1998[r]	2,262	496	1,766	1,763	387	1,376
1999	2,118	516	1,602	1,637	399	1,238

Year	NET NEW ORDERS			BACKLOG AS OF DECEMBER 31		
	TOTAL	Military	Non-Military	TOTAL	Military	Non-Military
1985	$3,823	$1,323	$2,500	$4,513	$2,261	$2,252
1986	1,985	1,224	761	3,503	1,689	1,814
1987	3,335	1,995	1,340	3,849	2,121	1,728
1988	3,507	1,623	1,884	3,985	1,998	1,987
1989	6,113	2,475	3,638	6,410	2,595	3,815
1990	2,692	1,891	801	6,230	2,887	3,343
1991	5,661	1,087	4,574	8,422	2,327	6,095
1992	3,124	2,097	1,027	8,310	2,729	5,581
1993	1,708	710	998	6,543	1,903	4,640
1994	1,879	484	1,395	6,035	1,390	4,645
1995	2,805	444	2,361	6,630	1,065	5,565
1996	1,868	745	1,123	5,873	1,108	4,765
1997	2,009	477	1,532	5,568	1,023	4,545
1998[r]	2,395	655	1,740	4,263	1,102	3,161
1999	4,891	672	4,219	6,179	1,008	5,171

Source: Bureau of the Census, "Aerospace Industry (Orders, Sales, and Backlog)" Series MA37D (Annually).
  a   Based on AIA's aerospace composite price deflator, 1987=100.
  r   Revised.

U.S. GOVERNMENT SPACECRAFT RECORD[a]
Calendar Years 1957–1999

Year	Earth Orbit[b] Success	Earth Orbit[b] Failure	Earth Escape[b] Success	Earth Escape[b] Failure	Year	Earth Orbit[b] Success	Earth Orbit[b] Failure	Earth Escape[b] Success	Earth Escape[b] Failure
1957	—	1	—	—	1982	21	—	—	—
1958	5	8	—	4	1983	31	—	—	—
1959	9	9	1	2	1984	35	3	—	—
1960	16	12	1	2	1985	37	1	—	—
1961	35	12	—	2	1986	11	4	—	—
1962	55	12	4	1	1987	9	1	—	—
1963	62	11	—	—	1988	16	1	—	—
1964	69	8	4	—	1989	24	—	2	—
1965	93	7	4	1	1990	40	—	1	—
1966	94	12	7	1[c]	1991	32[d]	—	—	—
1967	78	4	10	—	1992	26[d]	—	1	—
1968	61	15	3	—	1993	28[d]	1	1	—
1969	58	1	8	1	1994	31[d]	1	1	—
1970	36	1	3	—	1995	24[d]	2	1	—
1971	45	2	8	1	1996	30[d]	1	3	—
1972	33	2	8	—	1997	22	—	1	—
1973	23	2	3	—	1998	23	—	2	—
1974	27	2	1	—	1999[f]	23	4	2	—
1975	30	4	4	—					
1976	33	—	1	—	**TOTAL**	1,440	153	94	15
1977	27	2	2	—					
1978	34	2	7	—					
1979	18	—	—	—					
1980	16	4	—	—					
1981	20	1	—	—					

Source: NASA, "Aeronautics and Space Report of the President" (Annually).
  a Payloads, rather than launchings; some launches account for multiple spacecraft. Includes spacecraft from cooperating countries launched on U.S. launch vehicles.
  b The criterion of success is attainment of Earth orbit or Earth escape rather than judgement of mission success. "Escape" flights include all that were intended to go at least an altitude equal to the lunar distance from the Earth.
  c This Earth-escape failure did attain Earth orbit and therefore is included in the Earth-orbit success totals.
  d Excludes commercial satellites.
  f Through September 30.

WORLDWIDE SPACE LAUNCHINGS[a]
WHICH ATTAINED EARTH ORBIT OR BEYOND
Calendar Years 1957–1999

Country	Total 1957–1999	1995	1996	1997	1998	1999[c]
TOTAL..............................	4,029	76	72	76	80	55
U.S.S.R.	2,593	33	25	19	25	24
United States	1,179	27	32	37	36	23
European Space Agency	113	12	10	11	11	5
Japan	54	1	1	2	2	—
People's Republic of China ...	56	2	3	6	6	2
India................................	11	—	1	1	—	1
Israel	3	1	—	—	—	—
Other[b]	20	—	—	—	—	—

Source: NASA, "Aeronautics and Space Report of the President" (Annually).
  a   Number of launchings rather than spacecraft; some launches orbited multiple spacecraft.
  b   Includes 10 by France, 8 by Italy (5 were U.S. spacecraft), 1 by Australia, and 1 by the United Kingdom.
  c   Through September 30.

U.S. SPACE LAUNCH VEHICLES
As of 1999

Vehicle and Initial Launch & First Launch of this Modification	Stages	Thrust (Kilo-newtons)	Maximum Payload (Kg)[a]		
			185-Km Orbit	Geo-synch.-Transfer Orbit	Circular Sun-Synch. Orbit
Pegasus (1990)	1. Orion 50S* 2. Orion 50* 3. Orion 38*	484.9 118.2 31.9	380 280[b]	—	210
Pegasus XL (1994)[c]	1. Orion 50S-XL* 2. Orion 50-XL* 3. Orion 38*	743.3 201.5 31.9	460 350[b]	—	335
Taurus (1994)	0. Castor 120* 1. Orion 50S* 2. Orion 50* 3. Orion 38*	1,687.7 580.5 138.6 31.9	1,400 1,080[b]	255	1,020
Delta II 7900 Series (1960; 1990)	1. RS-270/A plus 9 Hercules GEM* 2. AJ10-118K 3. Star 48B*	1,043.0 4,388.4 42.4 66.4	5,089 3,890[b]	1,842[d]	3,175
Delta III (1998)[c]	1. RS-27 plus 9 Alliant GEM* 2. RL-10B 3. Star 48B*	1,043.0 5,479.2 110.0 66.4	8,292	3,810	6,768
Atlas E (1958; 1968)	1. Atlas MA-3	1,739.5	820[b] 1,860[bf]	—	910[f]
Atlas I (1966; 1990)	1. Atlas MA-5 2. 2 Centaur I	1,952.0 146.8	—	2,255	—
Atlas II (1966; 1991)	1. Atlas MA-5A 2. 2 Centaur II	2,110.0 146.8	6,580 5,510[b]	2,810	4,300
Atlas IIA (1966; 1992)	1. Atlas MA-5A 2. 2 Centaur II	2,110.0 185.1	6,828 6,170[b]	3,062	4,750
Atlas IIAS (1966; 1993)	1. Atlas MA-5A plus 4 Castor IV* 2. 2 Centaur II	2,110.0 1,734.4 185.1	8,640 7,300[b]	3,606	5,800

(Continued on next page)

U.S. SPACE LAUNCH VEHICLES
As of 1999 (Continued)

Vehicle and Initial Launch & First Launch of this Modification	Stages	Thrust (Kilo-newtons)	Maximum Payload (Kg)[a]		
			185-Km Orbit	24-Hour Polar Orbit	Circular Sun-Synch. Orbit
Titan II (1964; 1988)	1. 2 LR-87 2. LR-91	2,090.0 440.0	1,905 [b]	—	—
Titan III (1964; 1989)	0. 2 5 1/2-segment, 3.05-m. dia* 1. 2 LR-87 2. LR-91	12,420.0 2,429.0 462.8	14,515	5,000[g]	—
Titan IV (1989)	0. 2 7-segment, 3.05-m. dia* 1. 2 LR-87 2. LR-91	14,000.0 2,429.0 462.8	17,700 14,110[b]	6,350[g]	—
Titan IV/Centaur (1994)	0. 2 7-segment, 4.3-m. dia* 1. 2 LR-87 2. LR-91 3. Centaur 4. SRMU	14,000.0 2,429.0 462.5 73.4 7,690.0	—	5,760	—
Space Shuttle (reusable) (1981)	0. 3 main engines (SSMEs) fire in parallel with solid-fueled rocket boosters (SRBs) 1. 2 SRBs mounted on external tank (ET) fire in parallel with SSMEs 2. 2 OMS	5,006.1 23,580.0 53.4	24,900[h]	5,900[i]	—

Source: NASA, "Aeronautics and Space Report of the President" (Annually) and NASA Historian's office.
* Solid propellant; all others are liquid.
a Due east launch except as indicated.
b Polar launch.
c First launch was a failure.
d With Star 48B.
f With TE-M-364-4 upper stage.
g With appropriate upper stage.
h In full performance configuration (280–420 km orbit).
i With IUS or TOS.

FEDERAL SPACE ACTIVITIES OUTLAYS
Fiscal Years 1961–1999
(Millions of Current Dollars)

Year	TOTAL	NASA[a]	DoD	Energy	Commerce	Other[b]
1961	$ 1,468	$ 694	$ 710	$ 64	$ —	$ —
1962	2,387	1,226	1,029	130	1	1
1963	4,079	2,517	1,368	181	12	1
1964	5,930	4,131	1,564	220	12	3
1965	6,886	5,035	1,592	232	24	3
1966	7,719	5,858	1,637	188	28	7
1967	7,237	5,337	1,673	184	39	5
1968	6,667	4,595	1,890	147	29	6
1969	6,326	4,078	2,095	118	31	5
1970	5,453	3,565	1,756	103	24	5
1971	4,999	3,171	1,693	97	30	8
1972	4,772	3,195	1,470	60	37	10
1973	4,719	3,069	1,557	51	29	13
1974	4,854	2,960	1,777	39	64	14
1975	4,891	2,951	1,831	34	64	11
1976	5,314	3,336	1,864	26	71	16
Tr.Qtr.	1,361	869	458	8	23	4
1977	5,559	3,600	1,833	22	87	18
1978	6,188	3,582	2,457	29	101	20
1979	6,808	3,744	2,892	55	97	21
1980	7,734	4,340	3,162	49	89	94
1981	9,238	4,877	4,131	47	81	102
1982	10,542	5,463	4,772	60	142	106
1983	12,668	6,101	6,247	40	178	103
1984	14,813	6,461	8,000	33	209	109
1985	17,353	6,607	10,441	34	155	115
1986	18,683	6,756	11,449	35	317	127
1987	21,948	7,254	14,264	37	262	130
1988	23,521	8,451	14,397	199	334	140
1989	25,255	10,195	14,504	97	306	153
1990	25,788	12,292	12,962	79	279	177
1991	28,484	13,351	14,432	251	266	184
1992	27,998	12,838	14,437	223	298	202
1993	27,537	13,092	13,779	165	295	206
1994	23,929	12,363	10,973	83	297	213
1995	24,700	12,593	11,494	70	330	213
1996	24,675	12,694	11,353	46	354	228
1997	25,620[r]	13,055	11,959	37	336	233[r]
1998	25,753	12,866	12,230	97	326	234
1999[E]	25,617	12,375	12,453	103	431	255

Source: NASA, "Aeronautics and Space Report of the President" (Annually).
a   Excludes amounts for air transportation.
b   Departments of Interior, Transportation, and Agriculture, the National Science Foundation, and the Environmental Protection Agency.
E   Estimated.
Tr.Qtr.   See Glossary.
r   Revised.

FEDERAL SPACE ACTIVITIES BUDGET AUTHORITY
Fiscal Years 1961–1999
(Millions of Dollars)

Year	TOTAL	NASA[a]	DoD	Energy	Commerce	Other[b]
1961	$ 1,809	$ 926	$ 814	$ 68	$ —	$ 1
1962	3,295	1,797	1,298	148	51	1
1963	5,435	3,626	1,550	214	43	2
1964	6,831	5,016	1,599	210	3	3
1965	6,956	5,138	1,574	229	12	3
1966	6,971	5,065	1,689	187	27	3
1967	6,710	4,830	1,664	184	29	3
1968	6,529	4,430	1,922	145	28	4
1969	5,976	3,822	2,013	118	20	3
1970	5,340	3,547	1,678	103	8	4
1971	4,740	3,101	1,512	95	27	5
1972	4,575	3,071	1,407	55	31	11
1973	4,825	3,093	1,623	54	40	15
1974	4,641	2,759	1,766	42	60	14
1975	4,913	2,915	1,892	30	64	12
1976	5,319	3,225	1,983	23	72	16
Tr.Qtr.	1,341	849	460	5	22	5
1977	5,983	3,440	2,412	22	91	18
1978	6,518	3,623	2,738	34	103	20
1979	7,243	4,030	3,036	59	98	20
1980	8,761	4,680	3,848	40	93	100
1981	10,053	4,992	4,828	41	87	105
1982	12,518	5,528	6,679	61	145	105
1983	15,672	6,328	9,019	39	178	108
1984	17,445	6,858	10,195	34	236	122
1985	20,273	6,925	12,768	34	423	123
1986	21,764	7,165	14,126	35	309	129
1987	26,558	9,809	16,287	48	278	136
1988	26,738	8,322	17,679	241	352	144
1989	28,563	10,097	17,906	97	301	162
1990	27,588	11,460	15,616	79	243	190
1991	27,924	13,046	14,181	251	251	195
1992	28,991	13,199	15,023	223	327	219
1993	27,868	13,064	14,106	165	324	209
1994	26,789	13,022	13,166	74	312	215
1995	23,816	12,543	10,644	60	352	217
1996	24,833	12,569	11,514	46	472	232
1997	24,905 [r]	12,457	11,727	35	448	238 [r]
1998	25,451	12,321	12,359	97	435	239
1999 [E]	26,599	12,459	13,203	102	575	260

Source: NASA, "Aeronautics and Space Report of the President" (Annually).
  a Excludes amounts for air transportation.
  b Departments of Interior, Transportation, and Agriculture, the National Science Foundation, and the Environmental Protection Agency.
  E Estimated.
Tr.Qtr. See Glossary.
  r Revised.

NATIONAL AERONAUTICS AND SPACE ADMINISTRATION
OUTLAYS
Fiscal Years 1980–2001
(Millions of Current Dollars)

Year	TOTAL	Research and Development	Space Flight Control and Data Communications[a]	Construction of Facilities	Research & Program Management[b]
1980	$ 4,852	$3,701	$ —	$140	$1,010
1981	5,421	4,223	—	147	1,051
1982	6,035	4,796	—	109	1,130
1983	6,664	5,316	—	108	1,240
1984	7,048	2,792 [a]	2,915	109	1,232
1985	7,318	2,118	3,707	170	1,323
1986	7,404	2,615	3,267	189	1,332
1987	7,591	2,436	3,597	149	1,409
1988	9,092	2,916	4,362	166	1,648
1989	11,052	3,922	5,030	190	1,909
1990	12,429	5,094	5,117	218	2,000
1991	13,878	5,765	5,590	326	2,196
1992	13,961	6,579	5,118	463	1,802
1993	14,305	7,086	5,025	557	1,638
1994	13,695	6,758	4,899	371	1,666
1995 [c]	5,098	3,286	1,409	305	98
1996 [c]	1,022	510	241	265	6
1997 [c]	317	101	92	122	2
1998 [c]	138	40	34	64	—
1999 [c]	47	18	2	27	—
2000 [cE]	66	29	12	25	—
2001 [cE]	8	—	2	6	—

Year	TOTAL	Science, Aeronautics, & Technology	Human Space Flight	Other[b]	Mission Support
1995 [c]	$ 8,280	$2,708	$3,528	$ 15	$2,029
1996 [c]	12,858	5,017	5,452	16	2,373
1997 [c]	14,043	5,891	5,656	19	2,477
1998 [c]	14,068	6,015	5,551	19	2,483
1999 [c]	13,617	5,785	5,417	20	2,395
2000 [cE]	13,381	5,366	5,457	21	2,537
2001 [cE]	13,668	5,636	5,454	22	2,556

Source: Office of Management and Budget, "Budget of the United States Government" (Annually).
NOTE: Detail may not add to totals because of rounding.
   a Separate budget category beginning in 1984; funds formerly included under Research and Development.
   b Includes trust funds, Office of Inspector General, & GSA building delegation.
   c 1995 featured major budget account restructuring. Note: 1995–2001 outlays split between old and new account structure.
   E Estimate. Latest year reflects Administration's budget proposal.

NATIONAL AERONAUTICS AND SPACE ADMINISTRATION
BUDGET AUTHORITY
Fiscal Years 1971–2001
(Millions of Current Dollars)

Year	TOTAL	Research and Development	Space Flight Control and Data Communications[a]	Construction of Facilities	Research & Program Management[b]
1971	$ 3,312	$2,556	$ —	$ 26	$ 730
1972	3,308	2,523	—	53	732
1973	3,408	2,599	—	79	730
1974	3,040	2,194	—	101	745
1975	3,231	2,323	—	143	765
1976	3,552	2,678	—	82	792
Tr.Qtr.	932	700	—	11	221
1977	3,819	2,856	—	118	845
1978	4,064	3,012	—	162	890
1979	4,559	3,477	—	148	934
1980	5,243	4,088	—	159	996
1981	5,522	4,334	—	117	1,071
1982	6,020	4,772	—	114	1,134
1983	6,875	5,539	—	139	1,197
1984	7,316	2,064[a]	3,772	223	1,256
1985	7,573	2,468	3,594	178	1,332
1986	7,807	2,619	3,670	176	1,342
1987	10,923	3,154	6,100	217	1,453
1988	9,062	3,280	3,806	213	1,763
1989	10,969	4,213	4,555	275	1,927
1990	12,324	5,225	4,645	218	2,023
1991	14,016	6,024	5,271	498	2,212
1992	14,317	6,848	5,352	525	1,576
1993	14,310	7,074	5,059	526	1,652
1994	14,570	7,534	4,835	493	1,708

Year	TOTAL	Science, Aeronautics, & Technology	Human Space Flight	Other[b]	Mission Support
1995[c]	$13,854	$5,936	$5,515	$(130)	$2,533
1996	13,886	5,929	5,457	17	2,483
1997	13,711	5,590	5,540	19	2,562
1998	13,649	5,690	5,560	19	2,380
1999	13,655	5,654	5,480	21	2,500
2000[E]	13,602	5,581	5,468	21	2,532
2001[E]	14,036	5,929	5,500	23	2,584

Source: Office of Management and Budget, "Budget of the United States Government" (Annually).
NOTE: Detail may not add to totals because of rounding.
 a Separate budget category beginning in 1984; funds formerly included under Research and Development.
 b Includes trust funds, Office of the Inspector General, & GSA building delegation.
 c 1995 features major budget account restructuring.
 E Estimate. Latest year reflects Administration's budget proposal.
Tr.Qtr. See Glossary.

NATIONAL AERONAUTICS AND SPACE ADMINISTRATION BUDGET AUTHORITY BY MAJOR BUDGET ACCOUNT FOR SELECTED PROGRAMS

Fiscal Years 1999–2001
(Millions of Dollars)

	1999	2000[E]	2001[E]
HUMAN SPACE FLIGHT	$5,480	$5,468	$5,500
International Space Station	$2,300	$2,323	$2,115
Space Shuttle—**Total**	2,998	2,980	3,166
Shuttle Operations	2,427	2,547	NA
Safety/Performance Upgrades	572	439	NA
Payload & Utilization Operations	182	165	220
SCIENCE, AERONAUTICS, & TECHNOLOGY	$5,654	$5,581	$5,929
Space Science	$2,119	$2,193	$2,399
Life & Microgravity Sciences & Applications	264	275	302
Earth Science	1,414	1,443	1,406
Aeronautics & Space Transportation Technology	1,339	1,125	1,193
Mission Communication Services	380	406	(a)
Space Operations	—	—	529[a]
Academic Programs	139	139	100
MISSION SUPPORT	$2,500	$2,532	$2,584
Safety, Mission Assurance, Engineering & Advanced Concepts	$ 36	$ 43	$ 48
Space Communication Services	186	90	(a)
Research & Program Management	2,110	2,218	2,291
Construction of Facilities	169	182	246
INSPECTOR GENERAL	$ 20	$ 20	$ 22

Source: "NASA Budget Briefing Background Material" (Annually).
Note: Detail may not add to totals because of rounding.
  a   Mission & Space Communications merged in 2001.
  E   Estimate. Latest year reflects Administration's budget proposal.
 NA Not available.

DEPARTMENT OF DEFENSE SPACE PROGRAMS
PROCUREMENT (INCLUDING INITIAL SPARES) AND RDT&E
Fiscal Years 1999, 2000, and 2001
(Millions of Dollars[a])

Agency and Program	1999		2000 [E]		2001 [E]	
	Procurement	RDT&E	Procurement	RDT&E	Procurement	RDT&E
AIR FORCE						
Defense Support Program...	$ 87.0	$ 14.0	$108.4	$ 7.4	$106.4	$ 9.5
EELV..............................	—	242.0	68.1	318.0	288.0	332.9
Medium Launch Vehicles...	172.3	3.5	64.0	—	55.9	—
Milstar	—	514.0	—	357.2	—	236.8
NAVSTAR GPS	87.8	101.6	125.4	107.5	210.3	250.2
SBIRS-Low	—	181.3	—	225.6	—	241.0
SBIRS-High	—	508.5	—	420.5	—	569.2
Space Based Laser[b]	—	32.6	—	72.8	—	137.7
Titan Launch Vehicles	535.6	69.8	429.2	44.8	469.7	25.8
ARMY						
DSCS	$108.7	$ 15.2	$ 80.3	$ 8.9	$ 83.2	$ 9.9

Source: Department of Defense, "Program Acquisition Costs by Weapon System" (Annually).
    a Total Obligational Authority.
    b Air Force and BMDO funding.
    E Estimate. Latest year reflects Administration's budget proposal.
  NA Not available.
KEY: DSCS = Defense Satellite Communications System
      EELV = Evolved Expendable Launch Vehicle
      GPS = Global Positioning System
      SBIRS = Space-Based InfraRed System

PRELIMINARY FIGURES FROM THE INTERNATIONAL CIVIL AVI-ation Organization (ICAO) indicate total operating revenues for the world's scheduled airlines of $307 billion in 1999, up from $296 billion in 1998. Operating profits fell to $12.5 billion from $16 billion, due in part to a 5% increase in operating expenses which grew to $294 billion in 1999. The "net result" for 1999 (which accounts for income taxes and a number of other factors in addition to flight operations, such as: interest payments, subsidies, and the financial performance of affiliated companies) was $7.5 billion, down from $8.2 billion in 1998. As a percentage of operating revenues, the net result fell for the second year—down to 2.4% in 1999 from 2.8% in 1998.

Worldwide traffic growth remained strong in 1999. ICAO's preliminary statistics showed an increase of 5.8% in total ton-miles performed (passengers, baggage, freight, and mail) to 253 billion. The world's airlines carried 1.56 billion passengers (up 5.9%) and 31 million tons of freight (up 6.5%). The passenger load factor returned to 69%, up from 68% in 1998.

After recording an all-time high of $9.3 billion in 1998, operating profits for U.S. air carriers fell sharply (16%) to $7.9 billion, according to preliminary figures from the Department of Transportation. The 1999 profit comprised revenues totaling $118 billion (up $4.9 billion) and expenses totaling $110 billion (up $6.3 billion).

Domestic operations accounted for 76% of U.S. airline revenue, which reached $91 billion, up from $86 billion the previous year.

International operations generated revenues of $28 billion, up $839 million.

U.S. air carriers experienced traffic gains in domestic and international operations. In 1999, U.S. scheduled airlines flew a record 87 billion revenue ton-miles, which compares with 82 billion in 1998. Passenger ton-miles totaled 65 billion (up from 62 billion), and cargo ton-miles amounted to 22 billion (up from 20 billion).

Total boardings increased 3.7% to a record 635 million passengers for U.S. scheduled air carriers in 1999, with 582 million in domestic operations and 53 million in international operations. The revenue passenger load factor dropped slightly for domestic service to 70%, but rose for international operations to 74%.

The fleet of turbine-engined aircraft in airline service increased by 1,126 to 24,128, according to the annual "Air World Survey," sponsored by Exxon International. The turbojet fleet grew 832, while the number of turboprops increased 216. Turbine-powered helicopters in airline service rose 5.7% to 1,449. The total number of U.S.-built aircraft in world airline service was 13,537, or 56.1% of the total. With the exception of a brief rise in 1998 to 57.1%, the U.S. share has declined steadily since 1986. U.S. manufacturers produced 67.5% of the 15,453 jet aircraft in service.

The U.S. air carrier fleet grew 1.4% in 1999 to 8,228 aircraft. The turbojet fleet grew by 219 to 5,630. The number of turboprops declined 44 to 1,788, according to data from the Federal Aviation Administration.

OPERATING REVENUES AND EXPENSES
OF WORLD SCHEDULED AIRLINES[a]
Calendar Years 1996–1999
(Millions of U.S. Dollars)

	1996	1997	1998	1999[p]
OPERATING REVENUES:				
Scheduled Services:				
Passenger	$216,710	$221,820	$226,100	
Freight	27,830	29,720	29,420	
Mail	2,490	2,530	2,360	
				NA
Total Scheduled Services	$247,030	$254,070	$257,880	
Non-Scheduled Services	11,740	11,250	9,660	
Incidental	23,730	25,680	27,960	
Total Operating Revenues	$282,500	$291,000	$295,500	$306,500
OPERATING EXPENSES:				
Flight Operations	$ 74,810	$ 76,390	$ 75,080	
Maintenance & Overhaul	28,540	30,310	31,190	
Depreciation & Amortization ...	19,100	17,990	18,280	
User Charges & Station				NA
Expenses	47,920	47,690	50,010	
Passenger Services	29,090	29,310	29,770	
Ticketing, Sales & Promotion ...	41,320	40,700	40,110	
General, Administrative & Other	29,420	32,310	35,160	
Total Operating Expenses............	$270,200	$274,700	$279,600	$294,000
OPERATING RESULT	$ 12,300	$ 16,300	$ 15,900	$ 12,500
Percent of Revenue.................	4.4%	5.6%	5.4%	4.1%
NET RESULT[b]	$ 5,300	$ 8,550	$ 8,200	$ 7,500
Percent of Revenue.................	1.9%	2.9%	2.8%	2.4%

Source: International Civil Aviation Organization, "Civil Aviation Statistics of the World" (Annually).
   a   Excludes domestic operations in the Commonwealth of Independent States.
   b   Net Result equals Operating Result minus non-operating items, including interest, income taxes, retirement of property and
       equipment, affiliated companies, and subsidies.
   NA   Not available.
   p   Preliminary.

TRAFFIC STATISTICS
WORLD AIRLINE SCHEDULED SERVICE[a]
Calendar Years 1970–1999

Year	Passengers Carried	Freight Tons Carried	Passenger-Miles Performed	Seat-Miles Available	Passenger Load Factor	Ton-Miles Performed		TOTAL (Passengers & Baggage, Freight, Mail)
						Freight	Mail	
	(Millions)		(Billions)		(Percent)	(Millions)		
1970	383	6.7	286	522	55%	8,230	2,100	38,820
1971	411	7.4	307	568	54	9,060	1,990	41,420
1972	450	8.0	348	609	57	10,290	1,900	46,690
1973	489	9.1	384	667	58	12,010	1,970	51,910
1974	515	9.5	408	688	59	13,030	1,980	55,270
1975	534	9.6	433	733	59	13,270	1,990	58,080
1976	576	10.3	475	789	60	14,750	2,080	63,880
1977	610	11.1	508	837	61	16,190	2,170	68,790
1978	679	11.7	582	902	65	17,770	2,240	77,770
1979	754	12.1	659	999	66	19,190	2,350	86,890
1980	748	12.2	677	1,071	63	20,120	2,520	89,720
1981	752	12.0	695	1,092	64	21,150	2,600	92,810
1982	766	12.8	710	1,115	64	21,600	2,650	94,840
1983	798	13.5	739	1,151	64	24,050	2,740	100,280
1984	848	14.8	794	1,226	65	27,170	2,950	109,050
1985	899	15.1	850	1,293	66	27,290	3,010	114,860
1986	960	16.2	902	1,389	65	29,580	3,110	122,470
1987	1,028	17.7	988	1,471	67	33,100	3,220	134,570
1988	1,082	19.0	1,060	1,568	68	36,480	3,310	145,290
1989	1,109	19.9	1,102	1,621	68	39,140	3,460	152,730
1990	1,165	20.3	1,177	1,740	68	40,270	3,650	161,110
1991	1,135	19.3	1,147	1,727	66	40,110	3,480	158,030
1992	1,146	19.5	1,199	1,821	66	42,900	3,510	165,850
1993	1,142	19.9	1,211	1,872	65	46,880	3,580	171,660
1994	1,233	22.6	1,305	1,969	66	52,890	3,710	187,280
1995	1,304	24.5	1,397	2,087	67	56,940	3,860	201,320
1996	1,391	25.6	1,511	2,214	68	61,100	3,970	217,230
1997	1,457	29.1	1,599	2,316	69	70,470	4,100	235,750
1998	1,471	29.2	1,632	2,383	68	69,710	3,950	238,680
1999[p]	1,558	31.1	1,732	2,507	69	74,000	3,900	252,600

Source: International Civil Aviation Organization (ICAO).
a Includes international and domestic traffic on scheduled service performed by the airlines of the 185 states which were members of ICAO in 1999.
p Preliminary.

OPERATING REVENUES AND EXPENSES OF U.S. AIR CARRIERS[a]
DOMESTIC AND INTERNATIONAL OPERATIONS
Calendar Years 1965–1999
(Millions of Dollars)

Year	TOTAL OPERATIONS[b]			Domestic Operations			International Operations		
	Operating Revenues	Operating Expenses	Operating Profit (or Loss)	Operating Revenues	Operating Expenses	Operating Profit (or Loss)	Operating Revenues	Operating Expenses	Operating Profit (or Loss)
1965	$ 4,958	$ 4,286	$ 672	$ 3,691	$ 3,239	$ 452	$ 1,267	$ 1,047	$ 220
1966	5,745	4,970	775	4,171	3,670	502	1,574	1,300	274
1967	6,865	6,157	708	4,981	4,560	421	1,884	1,597	287
1968	7,753	7,248	505	5,691	5,397	295	2,062	1,852	210
1969	8,791	8,403	387	6,936	6,613	322	1,855	1,790	65
1970	9,290	9,247	43	7,180	7,181	(1)	2,109	2,066	44
1971	10,046	9,717	328	7,753	7,496	257	2,292	2,221	71
1972	11,163	10,578	584	8,652	8,158	493	2,512	2,420	91
1973	12,419	11,834	585	9,694	9,200	494	2,725	2,633	91
1974	14,703	13,978	725	11,546	10,761	785	3,157	3,218	(60)
1975	15,356	15,229	128	12,020	11,903	117	3,336	3,326	11
1976	17,503	16,781	721	13,899	13,324	575	3,605	3,457	147
1977	19,926	19,018	908	15,822	15,166	657	4,104	3,852	252
1978	22,892	21,527	1,366	18,189	17,172	1,018	4,703	4,355	348
1979	27,227	27,028	199	21,652	21,523	129	5,575	5,505	69
1980	33,728	33,949	(222)	26,404	26,409	(6)	6,543	6,766	(223)
1981	36,211	36,612	(401)	28,788	29,051	(264)	6,390	6,574	(184)
1982	36,066	36,804	(739)	28,728	29,478	(750)	6,435	6,452	(17)
1983	38,593	38,231	362	31,014	31,186	(171)	7,163	6,693	470
1984	44,060	41,946	2,114	35,394	33,812	1,582	7,975	7,485	490
1985	48,580	47,207	1,372	37,629	36,611	1,018	8,302	7,984	319
1986	50,086	48,855	1,231	41,001	39,984	1,060	8,621	8,458	163
1987	56,787	54,339	2,448	45,658	43,925	1,733	10,925	10,226	698
1988	63,679	60,236	3,443	50,187	47,739	2,448	13,402	12,403	998
1989	69,225	67,413	1,812	54,314	52,460	1,855	14,911	14,954	(43)
1990	75,984	77,898	(1,913)	57,994	58,983	(989)	17,990	18,914	(924)
1991	75,158	76,943	(1,785)	56,230	56,758	(528)	18,928	20,185	(1,257)
1992	78,140	80,585	(2,444)	57,654	58,801	(1,147)	20,486	21,784	(1,298)
1993	84,559	83,121	1,438	63,233	61,157	2,076	21,326	21,964	(637)
1994	88,313	85,600	2,713	65,949	63,758	2,191	22,364	21,842	522
1995	94,318	88,455	5,863	70,885	66,120	4,765	23,433	22,335	1,098
1996	101,937	95,728	6,209	76,891	71,573	5,317	25,047	24,155	892
1997	109,568	100,981	8,587	82,250	75,731	6,518	27,318	25,250	2,068
1998	113,465	104,137	9,328	86,494	78,389	8,105	26,971	25,749	1,223
1999[p]	118,327	110,476	7,851	90,518	84,344	6,173	27,810	26,132	1,677

Source: Department of Transportation, Office of Aviation Statistics, "Air Carrier Financial Statistics Quarterly" (Quarterly).
NOTE: Detail may not add to totals because of rounding.
   a   Scheduled and non-scheduled service for all certificated route air carriers. Excludes supplemental air carriers, commuters, and air taxis.
   b   For 1980 and subsequent years, includes 'Other' operations not reported as 'Domestic' or 'International.'
   p   Preliminary.

U.S. AIR CARRIERS
TOTAL ASSETS AND INVESTMENT IN EQUIPMENT
Calendar Years 1969–1999
(Millions of Dollars)

Year	TOTAL Assets	Value of Flight Equipment	Value of Ground Property & Equipment & Other[a]	Less: Reserves for Depreciation & Overhaul	Equals: Net Value of Owned Operating Property & Equipment	Investment in Operating Property and Equipment as a Percent of Total Assets
1969	$ 12,069	$ 9,943	$ 1,516	$ 3,560	$ 7,899	65.4%
1970	12,913	10,950	1,951	4,120	8,782	68.0
1971	12,998	11,221	2,028	4,649	8,600	66.2
1972	13,635	11,918	2,225	5,115	9,028	66.2
1973	14,464	12,908	2,424	5,693	9,639	66.6
1974	15,200	13,538	2,539	6,252	9,826	64.6
1975	15,064	14,035	2,635	6,823	9,847	65.4
1976	15,454	14,399	2,792	7,585	9,605	62.2
1977	16,869	14,822	2,997	8,141	9,679	57.4
1978	20,745	16,127	3,367	8,799	10,696	51.6
1979	24,907	18,561	3,985	9,746	12,800	51.4
1980	28,900	20,859	4,682	10,309	15,233	52.7
1981	30,513	22,375	5,175	11,028	16,521	54.1
1982	31,525	23,786	5,424	11,405	17,804	56.5
1983	35,213	26,588	6,191	12,910	19,868	56.4
1984	36,769	28,509	6,061	14,043	20,527	55.8
1985	40,978	30,402	6,772	15,467	21,707	53.0
1986	47,105	31,750	8,468	14,764	25,454	54.0
1987	51,436	33,177	9,223	15,580	26,820	52.1
1988	56,047	35,781	10,248	17,450	28,579	51.0
1989	62,454	38,812	11,903	19,018	31,697	50.8
1990	67,769	40,215	13,523	20,593	33,144	48.9
1991	70,332	42,897	14,285	22,009	35,173	50.0
1992	75,426	48,563	15,219	24,445	39,337	52.2
1993	82,399	51,513	15,438	24,949	42,003	51.0
1994	84,442	51,951	15,844	26,476	41,319	48.9
1995	89,782	56,018	16,804	29,056	43,766	48.7
1996	95,184	59,206	16,661	30,029	45,838	48.2
1997	105,226	66,523	17,643	32,789	51,377	48.8
1998	118,308	75,385	19,980	35,992	59,373	50.2
1999 [p]	133,156	85,837	21,780	38,901	68,716	51.6

Source: Department of Transportation, Office of Aviation Statistics, "Air Carrier Financial Statistics Quarterly" (Quarterly).
   a   Includes land and construction in progress.
   p   Preliminary.

SOURCES OF OPERATING REVENUES OF U.S. AIR CARRIERS[a]
DOMESTIC AND INTERNATIONAL OPERATIONS
Calendar Years 1985–1999
(Millions of Dollars)

Year	TOTAL Operating Revenues	Passenger Service[b]	Mail	Freight[b] & Air Express	Excess Baggage	Other[c]
DOMESTIC OPERATIONS						
1985	$37,629	$33,343	$ 733	$1,581	$ 78	$ 1,895
1986	41,001	33,814	679	4,278	85	2,159
1987	45,658	37,492	704	4,952	67	2,443
1988	50,187	41,002	789	5,807	72	2,518
1989	54,314	43,670	767	5,408	70	4,399
1990	57,994	46,282	747	4,276	76	6,613
1991	56,230	44,594	734	4,487	78	6,337
1992	57,654	45,246	937	4,655	87	6,729
1993	63,233	49,289	974	5,266	91	7,612
1994	65,949	50,504	971	5,844	98	8,531
1995	70,885	53,971	1,050	6,546	92	9,227
1996	76,891	59,381	1,024	7,029	94	9,362
1997	82,250	62,549	1,087	7,497	99	11,017
1998	86,494	64,847	1,423	7,711	105	12,408
1999[p]	90,518	67,708	1,472	7,783	118	13,436
INTERNATIONAL OPERATIONS						
1985	$ 8,302	$ 6,451	$ 161	$1,130	$ 28	$ 532
1986	8,621	6,551	154	1,451	28	437
1987	10,925	8,374	180	1,783	33	555
1988	13,402	10,357	183	2,150	39	672
1989	14,911	11,181	188	2,417	47	1,078
1990	17,990	13,468	223	2,602	43	1,654
1991	18,928	14,103	223	3,134	50	1,419
1992	20,486	15,664	247	2,980	47	1,547
1993	21,326	15,915	237	3,220	49	1,905
1994	22,364	16,300	212	3,606	46	2,201
1995	23,433	16,788	216	3,994	48	2,387
1996	25,047	17,337	255	4,664	47	2,743
1997	27,318	18,320	275	5,156	56	3,511
1998	26,971	17,667	285	5,278	50	3,692
1999[p]	27,810	17,927	263	5,868	46	3,705

Source: Department of Transportation, Office of Aviation Statistics, "Air Carrier Financial Statistics Quarterly" (Quarterly).
NOTE: Detail may not add to totals because of rounding.
  a Scheduled and non-scheduled service for all certificated route air carriers. Excludes supplemental air carriers, commuters, and air taxis.
  b Scheduled and charter.
  c Includes subsidy, reservation cancellation fees, miscellaneous operating revenues, and other transport-related revenues.
  p Preliminary.

OPERATING EXPENSES OF U.S. AIR CARRIERS[a]
DOMESTIC AND INTERNATIONAL OPERATIONS
Calendar Years 1985–1999
(Millions of Dollars)

Year	TOTAL Operating Expenses	Flying Operations	Maintenance	Passenger Service	Aircraft & Traffic Servicing	Promotion and Sales	Depreciation & Amortization	Other[b]
DOMESTIC OPERATIONS								
1985	$36,611	$12,684	$ 3,604	$3,464	$ 5,781	$ 6,089	$2,318	$ 2,670
1986	39,934	11,368	4,475	3,793	7,680	6,820	2,652	3,171
1987	43,925	12,509	4,951	4,169	8,575	7,399	2,855	3,468
1988	47,739	13,176	5,643	4,444	9,527	8,235	2,977	3,737
1989	52,460	14,749	6,184	4,775	9,449	8,718	3,078	5,507
1990	58,983	18,166	6,921	5,220	9,094	9,102	3,273	7,207
1991	56,758	16,831	6,682	5,068	9,140	8,856	3,217	6,964
1992	58,801	17,203	6,884	5,327	9,783	8,936	3,340	7,328
1993	61,157	17,622	7,025	5,241	10,172	9,387	3,621	8,089
1994	63,758	17,912	7,312	5,305	10,543	9,882	3,782	9,023
1995	66,120	18,926	7,656	5,281	11,103	9,974	3,762	9,417
1996	71,573	21,515	8,292	5,577	11,569	10,414	3,878	10,328
1997	75,731	22,156	9,475	5,854	12,058	10,780	3,940	11,469
1998	78,389	21,044	10,311	6,252	12,699	10,743	4,144	13,195
1999[p]	84,344	22,616	11,086	6,757	13,786	10,750	5,026	14,325
INTERNATIONAL OPERATIONS								
1985	$ 7,984	$ 2,738	$ 768	$ 852	$ 1,069	$ 1,414	$ 482	$ 662
1986	8,458	2,402	901	877	1,386	1,665	518	711
1987	10,226	2,836	1,096	1,059	1,749	2,094	533	860
1988	12,403	3,230	1,332	1,280	2,193	2,742	618	1,009
1989	14,954	3,919	1,724	1,454	2,483	3,108	746	1,520
1990	18,878	5,454	2,051	1,738	2,657	3,833	887	2,295
1991	20,185	5,636	2,152	1,861	2,831	4,602	892	2,210
1992	21,784	5,843	2,148	2,204	3,255	5,229	1,033	2,073
1993	21,964	5,928	1,967	2,175	3,072	5,339	1,077	2,406
1994	21,842	5,842	2,064	2,311	3,336	4,335	1,237	2,716
1995	22,335	6,181	2,273	2,467	3,748	3,527	1,106	3,033
1996	24,155	7,279	2,616	2,596	3,736	3,354	1,483	3,091
1997	25,250	7,462	2,899	2,736	3,823	3,476	1,281	3,571
1998	25,749	7,158	2,955	2,920	3,978	3,374	1,438	3,926
1999[p]	26,132	7,428	2,884	3,059	4,198	3,190	1,631	3,742

Source: Department of Transportation, Office of Aviation Statistics, "Air Carrier Financial Statistics Quarterly" (Quarterly).
NOTE: Detail may not add to totals because of rounding.
   a Scheduled and non-scheduled service for all certificated route air carriers. Excludes supplemental air carriers, commuters, and air taxis.
   b General and administrative and other transport-related expenses.
   p Preliminary.

TRAFFIC STATISTICS
U.S. AIR CARRIER SCHEDULED SERVICE[a]
Calendar Years 1965–1999

Year	Revenue Ton-Miles (Millions)			Total Available Ton-Miles (Millions)	Total Revenue Load Factor	Aircraft Revenue Miles (Millions)	Average Overall Flight Stage Length (Miles)	Average Available Seats per Aircraft Mile
	Passenger	Cargo[b]	Total					
1965	6,629	2,356	8,986	18,408	48.8%	1,354	322	96
1966	7,736	2,949	10,686	20,939	51.0	1,482	339	98
1967	9,561	3,475	13,036	26,968	48.3	1,834	371	101
1968	11,023	4,226	15,249	33,221	45.9	2,146	401	107
1969	12,197	4,701	16,898	38,664	43.7	2,385	443	112
1970	13,171	4,994	18,166	41,693	43.6	2,426	473	117
1971	13,565	5,120	18,685	44,139	42.3	2,378	476	125
1972	15,241	5,506	20,746	45,583	45.5	2,376	471	129
1973	16,196	6,046	22,242	49,019	45.4	2,448	477	135
1974	16,292	6,133	22,425	46,848	47.9	2,258	478	140
1975	16,281	5,905	22,186	47,254	46.9	2,241	476	143
1976	17,899	6,222	24,121	49,325	48.9	2,320	480	146
1977	19,322	6,587	25,909	52,284	49.6	2,419	490	149
1978	22,678	7,001	29,679	54,765	54.2	2,520	502	152
1979	26,202	7,189	33,390	60,844	54.9	2,791	517	154
1980	25,519	7,084	32,603	62,983	51.8	2,816	526	158
1981	24,889	7,060	31,949	61,186	52.2	2,703	519	161
1982	25,964	6,886	32,850	62,401	52.6	2,699	544	167
1983	28,183	7,573	35,756	65,385	54.7	2,809	558	169
1984	30,512	8,185	38,697	72,223	53.6	3,134	575	168
1985	33,640	7,689	41,329	76,059	54.3	3,320	569	168
1986	36,655	9,026	45,681	85,140	53.7	3,725	580	168
1987	40,453	10,016	50,469	92,209	54.7	3,988	606	167
1988	42,330	11,469	53,800	97,899	55.0	4,141	618	169
1989	43,271	12,187	55,458	100,082	55.4	4,193	633	169
1990	45,793	12,549	58,342	107,559	54.2	4,491	649	170
1991	44,795	12,130	56,925	105,599	53.9	4,416	651	169
1992	47,855	13,199	61,054	112,749	54.2	4,661	661	169
1993	48,968	14,120	63,088	115,473	54.6	4,846	669	166
1994	51,938	16,052	67,989	120,798	56.3	5,033	668	163
1995	54,066	16,921	70,987	126,154	56.3	5,293	657	160
1996	57,866	17,754	75,621	131,381	57.6	5,501	668	160
1997	60,342	20,510	80,852	137,544	58.8	5,659	696	160
1998[r]	61,809	20,496	82,304	141,722	58.1	5,838	704	159
1999	65,160	21,640	86,800	149,468	58.1	6,161	715	158

Source: Department of Transportation, Office of Aviation Statistics, "Air Carrier Traffic Statistics Monthly" (Monthly).
NOTE: Detail may not add to totals because of rounding.
    a Includes international and domestic operations.
    b Includes freight, air express, U.S. and foreign mail.
    r Revised.

PASSENGER STATISTICS
U.S. AIR CARRIER SCHEDULED SERVICE
DOMESTIC AND INTERNATIONAL OPERATIONS
Calendar Years 1985–1999

Year	Revenue Passenger Enplanements (Thousands)	Average Passenger Trip-Length (Miles)	Revenue Passenger Miles (Millions)	Available Seat Miles (Millions)	Revenue Passenger Load Factor[a]
DOMESTIC OPERATIONS					
1985	357,109	758	270,584	445,826	60.7
1986	393,864	767	302,090	497,991	60.7
1987	416,831	779	324,637	526,958	61.6
1988	419,210	786	329,309	536,663	61.4
1989	416,331	793	329,975	530,079	62.3
1990	423,565	803	340,231	563,065	60.4
1991	412,360	806	332,566	543,638	61.2
1992	431,693	806	347,931	557,989	62.4
1993	443,172	799	354,177	571,489	62.0
1994	481,755	787	378,990	585,438	64.7
1995	499,000	791	394,708	603,917	65.4
1996	530,708	802	425,596	626,389	67.9
1997	542,001	817	442,640	640,319	69.1
1998[r]	559,653	812	454,430	649,362	70.0
1999	582,326	824	479,689	686,940	69.8
INTERNATIONAL OPERATIONS					
1985	24,913	2,642	65,819	101,963	64.6
1986	25,082	2,570	64,456	109,445	58.9
1987	30,847	2,588	79,834	121,763	65.6
1988	35,404	2,655	93,992	140,140	67.1
1989	37,361	2,750	102,739	154,297	66.6
1990	41,995	2,803	117,695	170,310	69.1
1991	39,941	2,889	115,389	171,561	67.3
1992	43,415	3,009	130,622	194,784	67.1
1993	45,348	2,988	135,508	200,151	67.7
1994	47,093	2,981	140,391	198,893	70.6
1995	48,773	2,992	145,948	203,160	71.8
1996	50,526	3,029	153,067	208,682	73.3
1997	52,724	3,049	160,779	216,913	74.1
1998	53,232	3,074	163,656	224,728	72.8
1999	53,076	3,239	171,908	230,909	74.4

Source: Department of Transportation, Office of Aviation Statistics, "Air Carrier Traffic Statistics Monthly" (Monthly).
  a   Revenue passenger miles as a percent of available seat miles.
  r   Revised.

TURBINE-ENGINED AIRCRAFT IN THE WORLD AIRLINE FLEET
(By Model, 1995–1999)

	1995[a]	1996[a]	1997[a]	1998[a]	1999[a]
TOTAL AIRCRAFT IN SERVICE	20,041	21,127	22,110	23,002	24,128
Turbojets—TOTAL.................	12,810	13,425	14,024	14,621	15,453
Aerospatiale SE-210 Caravelle	27	20	12	12	12
Aerospatiale Corvette	—	—	—	—	2
Airbus A300........................	414	405	397	383	389
Airbus A310........................	218	222	224	227	220
Airbus A319........................	—	18	66	118	206
Airbus A320........................	510	549	612	685	773
Airbus A321........................	35	52	72	109	143
Airbus A330........................	38	49	63	87	131
Airbus A340........................	60	86	119	138	161
Antonov 72/74	4	8	8	9	9
Antonov 124	11	16	16	18	17
Antonov 225	—	1	1	1	1
Avro RJ-70/85/100	51	77	100	120	138
B.Ae./Aerospatiale Concorde	13	13	13	13	13
B.Ae. 146..........................	204	206	208	206	203
B.Ae. One-Eleven	112	121	122	105	101
B.Ae. (HS) 125	19	20	18	17	11
Beech 400 Beechjet	2	3	3	3	3
Boeing 707/720	123	122	112	98	94
Boeing 717	—	—	—	—	11
Boeing 727	1,346	1,363	1,322	1,263	1,189
Boeing 737	2,569	2,623	2,752	2,968	3,176
Boeing 747	963	996	1,040	1,042	1,041
Boeing 757	697	718	770	818	879
Boeing 767	580	628	663	710	752
Boeing 777	13	45	111	174	261
Canadair CL-601 Challenger...	2	2	2	2	2
Canadair Regional Jet...........	83	136	189	258	351
Cessna Citation I/II/III	44	45	41	35	34
Dassault Falcon 10/20/50	66	65	60	61	71
Embraer RJ135/RJ145	—	—	34	91	186
Fairchild 328 Jet	—	—	—	—	11
Fokker F-28 Fellowship	185	175	184	160	169
Fokker 70	23	34	36	42	42
Fokker 100	267	272	274	278	277
Gulfstream II/III/IV G-1159 ...	15	16	16	14	14
Ilyushin IL-62	106	105	105	86	83
Ilyushin IL-76	209	238	227	215	226
Ilyushin IL-86	51	98	80	75	79
Ilyushin IL-96	5	7	7	7	8
Israel Aircraft 1121/1124	13	11	11	18	10
Learjet	49	54	53	49	85
Lockheed L-1011 Tristar	190	190	169	156	135
Lockheed L-1329 Jetstar.........	3	3	1	1	1
MBB Hansa HFB-320............	13	16	16	17	9
McDonnell Douglas DC-8......	274	263	257	261	225
McDonnell Douglas DC-9......	787	785	759	749	714
McDonnell Douglas DC-10 ...	335	351	345	354	340
McDonnell Douglas MD-11 ...	146	159	171	180	187

(Continued on next page)

TURBINE-ENGINED AIRCRAFT IN THE WORLD AIRLINE FLEET
(By Model, 1995–1999, continued)

	1995[a]	1996[a]	1997[a]	1998[a]	1999[a]
Turbojets (continued)					
McDonnell Douglas MD-80	1,115	1,120	1,142	1,154	1,180
McDonnell Douglas MD-90	14	36	62	97	109
Tupolev Tu-134	192	188	189	189	188
Tupolev Tu-154	379	422	451	438	446
Tupolev Tu-204	4	6	6	7	9
Yakolev Yak-40/42	231	267	313	303	326
Turbine-Powered					
Helicopters—TOTAL	774	851	1,014	1,371	1,449
Aerospatiale SA-315 Lama	2	2	2	2	2
Aerospatiale SA-316 Alouette III	3	5	5	5	5
Aerospatiale SA-318 Alouette II	1	2	1	1	1
Aerospatiale (Nurtanio) SA-330 Puma	22	20	20	18	22
Aerospatiale AS-332 Super Puma	69	70	78	73	72
Aerospatiale AS-350 Ecureuil/ Astar	40	49	104	112	125
Aerospatiale AS-355 Ecureuil 2/ Twinstar.............................	15	15	15	23	28
Aerospatiale SA-365 Dauphin II	24	25	26	26	36
Agusta A109	1	1	—	—	—
Bell (Agusta/Fuji) 204	5	4	4	2	4
Bell 205	19	16	14	11	15
Bell 206 Jetranger/Longranger ...	145	155	151	361	363
Bell 212	105	106	101	112	120
Bell 214	12	11	7	17	14
Bell 222 UT........................	1	2	2	3	2
Bell 230	—	—	—	3	—
Bell 407	—	—	1	44	53
Bell 412	25	25	31	55	56
Boeing 107	16	16	15	15	15
Boeing Vertol BV-234	9	10	9	9	9
Hughes (Kawasaki) 500/369D ...	12	12	17	16	13
Kamov Ka-26	—	—	16	16	19
Kamov Ka-32	2	2	2	—	—
MBB BK-117	2	2	2	13	10
MBB/Nurtanio Bo.105	58	58	67	103	101
Mil Mi-2	—	24	40	32	28
Mil Mi-6	—	—	6	6	6
Mil Mi-8	18	48	91	83	107
Mil Mi-14............................	—	1	1	1	1
Mil Mi-26............................	—	—	7	7	5
Sikorsky S-55T......................	4	6	6	6	—
Sikorsky S-58T......................	1	1	2	1	1
Sikorsky S-61	81	82	90	65	79
Sikorsky S-62	1	1	1	1	—
Sikorsky S-64	5	5	5	5	22
Sikorsky S-76	72	75	75	124	115

(Continued on next page)

TURBINE-ENGINED AIRCRAFT IN THE WORLD AIRLINE FLEET
(By Model, 1995–1999, continued)

	1995[a]	1996[a]	1997[a]	1998[a]	1999[a]
Turboprops—TOTAL..................	6,457	6,851	7,072	7,010	7,226
Aerospatiale N.262/Mohawk 298	13	9	9	11	12
Aerospatiale/Aeritalia ATR 42 ...	259	283	296	299	296
Aerospatiale/Aeritalia ATR 72 ...	158	177	177	202	222
Airtech CN-235	25	24	24	24	33
Antonov An-8	—	—	2	—	6
Antonov An-12	46	68	71	83	81
Antonov An-22	2	5	3	3	1
Antonov An-24/26/28/30/32	400	484	530	499	475
B.Ae. ATP............................	52	55	50	57	55
B.Ae. Vanguard	1	—	—	—	—
B.Ae. Viscount.......................	24	20	18	12	12
B.Ae. (HP-137) Jetstream 31	296	274	287	233	258
B.Ae. Jetstream 41	66	74	91	92	92
B.Ae. HS-748	126	126	125	124	118
Beech 18 Turbo	21	20	20	18	9
Beech 90 King Air	35	39	46	39	46
Beech 99	143	140	138	139	110
Beech 100 King Air	46	48	39	39	47
Beech 200/300 Super King Air ...	121	126	122	111	112
Beech 1300	5	5	9	6	9
Beech 1900C/D	371	389	430	467	469
Bristol 175 Britannia	1	1	—	—	—
Canadair CL-44	2	1	—	—	4
CASA/Nurtanio C-212 Aviocar ...	114	111	113	105	110
Cessna 208 Caravan I	458	528	608	601	647
Cessna F406 Caravan II	35	28	30	31	30
Cessna 425/441 Conquest I/II ...	4	5	14	19	19
Convair 580/600/640	111	114	107	107	106
DHC-2/3 Turbo Beaver/Otter ...	17	22	20	20	24
DHC-5 Buffalo	1	1	1	1	1
DHC-6 Twin Otter	395	394	395	371	365
DHC-7 Dash 7	70	75	69	71	69
DHC-8 Dash 8	365	408	424	444	489
Dornier DO-228	106	112	114	118	121
Dornier DO-328	42	59	61	73	83
Douglas DC-3T Turbo Express ...	2	1	1	1	3
Embraer EMB-110 Bandeirante...	192	211	200	199	199
Embraer EMB-120 Brasilia........	254	295	308	316	307
Embraer EMB-121 Xingu	—	—	2	2	3
Fokker/Fairchild F-27/FH-227 ...					
Friendship	315	312	318	278	276
Fokker 50	171	176	171	167	188
GAF Nomad	18	13	15	15	16
Grumman G-21 Turbo Goose ...	1	—	—	—	—
Grumman G-73 Turbo Mallard	5	5	5	5	6
Grumman G-159 Gulfstream I ...	39	34	30	27	27

(Continued on next page)

TURBINE-ENGINED AIRCRAFT IN THE WORLD AIRLINE FLEET
(By Model, 1995–1999, continued)

	1995[a]	1996[a]	1997[a]	1998[a]	1999[a]
Turboprops (continued)					
Handley Page Herald	15	10	2	1	1
Harbin YU-12 II	41	42	42	48	48
IAI Arava	2	2	3	3	4
Ilyushin IL-18	33	38	34	32	41
Ilyushin IL-114	2	2	2	2	3
LET L-410...........................	61	87	115	118	141
Lockheed L-188 Electra	51	53	36	44	43
Lockheed L-100/L-382 Hercules	56	56	45	35	44
Mitsubishi MU-2B	14	15	15	16	21
Nihon AMC YS-11	81	78	63	49	46
Pilatus Britten-Norman BN-2T					
Turbo Islander	2	5	6	6	5
Pilatus PC-6 Turbo Porter	25	28	30	24	23
Pilatus PC-XII	—	2	2	14	21
Piper PA-31T/42 Cheyenne ...	16	18	20	20	22
Piper T-1040	12	13	14	13	13
PZL (Antonov) An-28	6	6	3	3	27
Rockwell Turbo Commander	9	9	11	9	8
Saab SF-340A/B	355	379	396	432	414
Saab 2000	22	34	42	45	43
Shorts SC-5 Belfast	2	2	2	2	2
Shorts SC-7 Skyliner/Skyvan ...	35	35	32	30	27
Shorts 330	50	52	48	42	37
Shorts 360	106	104	103	93	102
Swearingen Merlin	38	45	53	55	58
Swearingen Metro	423	398	394	379	398
Transall C-160.....................	6	—	—	—	6
Xian (Antonov) Y-7	66	66	66	66	65
TOTAL AIRCRAFT IN SERVICE	20,041	21,127	22,110	23,002	24,128
Number Manufactured in U.S.	11,775	12,117	12,487	13,139	13,537
Percent Manufactured in U.S.	58.8%	57.4%	56.5%	57.1%	56.1%
Turbojet Aircraft in Service	12,810	13,425	14,024	14,621	15,453
Number Manufactured in U.S.	9,265	9,520	9,789	10,126	10,430
Percent Manufactured in U.S.	72.3%	70.9%	69.8%	69.3%	67.5%
Turboprop Aircraft in Service ...	6,457	6,851	7,072	7,010	7,226
Number Manufactured in U.S.	2,002	2,074	2,172	2,165	2,226
Percent Manufactured in U.S.	31.0%	30.3%	30.7%	30.9%	30.8%
Turbine-Powered Helicopters					
In Service	774	851	1,014	1,371	1,449
Number Manufactured in U.S.	508	523	526	848	881
Percent Manufactured in U.S.	65.6%	61.5%	51.9%	61.9%	60.8%

Source: Exxon International Company, "Air World Survey," compiled by Aviation Data Service, Inc. (Annually).
NOTE: The "Air World Survey" covers aircraft in airline service as of December 31. Excludes air taxi operators.
  a Includes aircraft operated in the Commonwealth of Independent State countries. Formerly grouped under Aeroflot and excluded from the summary.

PERCENT OF CIVIL TURBOJET ENGINE MARKET
BY MANUFACTURER AND AIRCRAFT MODEL
as of December 1999

Aircraft Manufacturer and Model	Total Installed Engines	Engine Manufacturers					
		P&W	GE	RR	CFM	IAE	Other
TOTAL ENGINES	39,278	15,015	5,606	4,047	7,114	1,048	6,448
PERCENT SHARE	100.0%	38.2%	14.3%	10.3%	18.1%	2.7%	16.4%
Airbus A300[a]	512	14%	86%	–%	–%	–%	–%
Airbus A300B4-600R ...	316	53	47	–	–	–	–
Airbus A310[a]	156	35	65	–	–	–	–
Airbus A310-300	294	44	56	–	–	–	–
Airbus A319	392	–	–	–	74	26	–
Airbus A320[a]	36	–	–	–	100	–	–
Airbus A320-200	1,492	–	–	–	60	40	–
Airbus A321	282	–	–	–	50	50	–
Airbus A330	254	50	16	35	–	–	–
Airbus A340	660	–	–	–	100	–	–
Antonov AN-72	6	–	–	–	–	–	100
Antonov AN-74	14	–	–	–	–	–	100
Antonov AN-124	72	–	–	–	–	–	100
AS Corvette..................	6	100	–	–	–	–	–
AS Caravelle	26	69	–	31	–	–	–
AS/BAe Concorde	52	–	–	100	–	–	–
Avro Int'l RJ	564	–	–	–	–	–	100
BAe 1-11	226	–	–	100	–	–	–
BAe 146	820	–	–	–	–	–	100
BAe/HS 125	32	6	–	19	–	–	75
Beech 400 Beechjet	6	100	–	–	–	–	–
Boeing B-707[a]	92	100	–	–	–	–	–
Boeing B-707-320C	412	100	–	–	–	–	–
Boeing B-717	24	–	–	100	–	–	–
Boeing B-720	8	100	–	–	–	–	–
Boeing B-727 series[a]	1,332	89	–	11	–	–	–
Boeing B-727-200 Adv F	555	100	–	–	–	–	–
Boeing B-727-200 ADV	1,956	100	–	–	–	–	–
Boeing B-737[a]	524	71	–	–	29	–	–
Boeing B-737-200 ADV	1,356	100	–	–	–	–	–
Boeing B-737-300	2,112	–	–	–	100	–	–
Boeing B-737-400	934	–	–	–	100	–	–
Boeing B-737-500	766	–	–	–	100	–	–
Boeing B-737-700	360	–	–	–	100	–	–
Boeing B-737-800	390	–	–	–	100	–	–
Boeing B-747[a]	2,036	50	39	11	–	–	–
Boeing B-747-200B	668	72	13	16	–	–	–
Boeing B-747-400	1,584	41	33	27	–	–	–
Boeing B-757[a]	294	27	–	73	–	–	–
Boeing B-757-200	1,474	46	–	54	–	–	–
Boeing B-767[a]	240	21	79	–	–	–	–
Boeing B-767-200ER	266	52	48	–	–	–	–
Boeing B-767-300	200	24	76	–	–	–	–
Boeing B-767-300ER	804	37	55	7	–	–	–
Boeing B-777[a]	194	57	39	34	–	–	–
Boeing B-777-200ER	322	20	50	29	–	–	–

(Continued on next page)

PERCENT OF CIVIL TURBOJET ENGINE MARKET
BY MANUFACTURER AND AIRCRAFT MODEL
(as of December 1999, continued)

Aircraft Manufacturer and Model	Total Installed Engines	Engine Manufacturers					
		P&W	GE	RR	CFM	IAE	Other
Canadair CL 600/601 ...	6	–%	67%	–%	–%	–%	33%
Canadair Regional Jet ...	414	–	100	–	–	–	–
Canadair Regional Jet 200	274	–	100	–	–	–	–
Cessna 500s	80	95	–	5	–	–	–
Cessna 650	20	–	–	–	–	–	100
Dassault Falcon	160	–	84	–	–	–	16
Embraer ERJ-135	26	–	–	–	–	–	100
Embraer ERJ-145	338	–	–	–	–	–	100
Fairchild Dornier 328 Jet	24	100	–	–	–	–	–
Fokker F-28...................	328	–	–	100	–	–	–
Fokker 70	84	–	–	100	–	–	–
Fokker 100	538	–	–	100	–	–	–
Gulfstream II/III/IV	34	–	–	100	–	–	–
IAI 1124/1125	20	–	–	–	–	–	100
Ilyushin IL-62	348	–	–	–	–	–	100
Ilyushin IL-76[a]	472	–	–	–	–	–	100
Ilyushin IL-76TD	424	–	–	–	–	–	100
Ilyushin IL-86	312	–	–	–	–	–	100
Ilyushin IL-96	32	–	–	–	–	–	100
Learjet 23/24/25............	118	–	100	–	–	–	–
Learjet 35/36/55/60	102	4	–	–	–	–	96
Lockheed JetStar............	4	–	–	–	–	–	100
Lockheed L-1011	522	–	–	100	–	–	–
MBB HFB-320 Hansa Jet	18	–	100	–	–	–	–
Douglas DC-8..............	996	63	–	–	37	–	–
Douglas DC-9[a]	532	100	–	–	–	–	–
Douglas DC-9-30	930	100	–	–	–	–	–
Douglas DC-10[a]...........	660	19	81	–	–	–	–
Douglas DC-10-30........	378	–	100	–	–	–	–
MDC MD-11 series[a]	204	25	75	–	–	–	–
MDC MD-11[b]..............	363	49	51	–	–	–	–
MDC MD-80s[a]	320	100	–	–	–	–	–
MDC MD-82	1,184	100	–	–	–	–	–
MDC MD-83	528	100	–	–	–	–	–
MDC MD-88	314	100	–	–	–	–	–
MDC MD-90	218	–	–	–	–	100	–
Rockwell Sabreliner	2	–	100	–	–	–	–
Tupolev TU-134............	392	–	–	–	–	–	100
Tupolev TU-154[a]	210	–	–	–	–	–	100
Tupolev TU-154B2	564	–	–	–	–	–	100
Tupolev TU-154M........	621	–	–	–	–	–	100
Tupolev TU-204............	20	–	–	–	–	–	100
Yakolev YAK-40............	756	–	–	–	–	–	100
Yakolev YAK-42............	267	–	–	–	–	–	100

Source: Aerospace Industries Association, based on data from Aviation Data Service.
  a Data for major (100 or more aircraft) series excluded and reported separately.
  b Series bearing same designation as model number, but qualifies for separate reporting as a major series.
KEY: AS = Aerospatiale; BAe = British Aerospace; CFM = CFM International; GE = General Electric;
     IAE = International Aero Engines; IAI = Israel Aircraft Industries; MBB = Messerschmitt Bolkow Blohm;
     MDC = McDonnell Douglas; P&W = Pratt & Whitney; RR = Rolls-Royce.

ACTIVE[a] U.S. AIR CARRIER FLEET
By Type of Aircraft, Number of Engines and Model
Active as of December 1995–1999

	1995	1996	1997	1998	1999
TOTAL	7,411	7,478	7,616	8,111	8,228
Turbojets—TOTAL	4,832	4,922	5,108	5,411 [r]	5,630
Four-Engine—TOTAL	435	440	450	447	441
Boeing 707	6	5	3	—	1
Boeing 747	189	195	201	201	188
B.Ae./AVRO 146	21	21	26	18	46
McDonnell Douglas DC-8	219	219	220	228	206
Three-Engine—TOTAL	1,210	1,212	1,224	1,238	1,181
Boeing 727	877	856	874	882	811
Lockheed L-1011	97	102	79	70	66
McDonnell Douglas DC-10/MD-11	236	254	271	286	304
Twin-Engine—TOTAL	3,187	3,270	3,434	3,726 [r]	4,008
Airbus A-300	53	62	68	61	68
Airbus A-310	23	27	28	39	39
Airbus A-319	—	—	2	23	40
Airbus A-320	104	113	119	143	162
BAe HS-125	—	—	—	—	1
Beech 400	—	—	—	1	1
Boeing 717	—	—	—	—	2
Boeing 737	1,055	1,055	1,077	1,080	1,179
Boeing 757	440	457	487	510	555
Boeing 767	210	213	234	261	278
Boeing 777	7	15	23	36	53
Canadair CL-600	35	53	77	152	187
Cessna C500/C501	—	—	—	10	9
Dassau AMD	—	—	—	27	27
Embraer ERJ-135	—	—	—	—	7
Embraer ERJ-145	—	—	11	55	95
Fokker F-28	155	155	142	147	145
Israel Aircraft 1124	—	—	—	1	1
Learjet LR-25	—	2	3	7	8
Learjet LR-31	—	—	—	1	1
Learjet LR-35	3	4	9	11	11
McDonnell Douglas DC-9/ MD-80/MD-90	1,102	1,114	1,154	1,158	1,133
Mitsubishi MU-300	—	—	—	2	5
North American NA-265	—	—	—	1	1
Turboprops—TOTAL	1,713 [r]	1,696 [r]	1,646 [r]	1,832 [r]	1,788
Four-Engine—TOTAL	81	56	45	39	28
Canadair CL44D	1	—	—	—	—
De Havilland DHC-7	16	12	5	7	6
Lockheed 188 Electra	43	23	22	17	14
Lockheed 382	21	21	18	15	8

(Continued on next page)

ACTIVE[a] U.S. AIR CARRIER FLEET (Continued)
By Type of Aircraft, Number of Engines, and Model
Active as of December 1995–1999

	1995	1996	1997	1998	1999
Twin-Engine—Total	1,632[r]	1,635[r]	1,596[r]	1,789[r]	1,759
Airtech CN-235	—	—	—	—	1
Beech BE90	1	3	2	8	6
Beech BE99	36	27	28	36	38
Beech BE100	1	2	1	2	4
Beech BE200	4	11	7	19	19
Beech BE1900	289	254	243	325	239
B.Ae. ATP	10	10	9	—	9
B.Ae. Jetstream	174	223	215	203	184
CASA C212 Aviocar	1	—	—	3	4
Cessna CE208B	—	—	—	137	167
Cessna C441	2	2	2	4	2
Convair 580/600/640	34	23	19	15	12
DeHavilland DHC-6	44	38	49	54	54
DeHavilland DHC-8	137	151	154	169	180
Dornier DO328	33	39	47	35	39
Embraer EMB110	14	3	1	1	1
Embraer EMB120	217	235	227	218	225
Fairchild/Fokker F-27/FH-227	35	36	44	38	38
Grumman G-73	5	5	5	5	3
Gulfstream 690A	—	—	1	—	—
Mitsubishi MU-2	—	3	11	13	14
Nihon YS-11	11	11	—	—	—
Piper PA31T	5	9	10	6	6
Piper 42	1	2	2	2	2
Saab-Fairchild SF340	219	226	253	271	275
Shorts SC-7	3	3	3	3	3
Shorts SD-3	38	39	33	15	20
SNAIS ATR-42	110	99	95	83	79
SNAIS ATR-72	51	51	55	60	60
Swearingen SA-226	13	9	7	4[r]	3
Swearingen SA-227	144	121	73	60	72
Single-Engine—TOTAL	—	5	5	4	1
Piston-Engine—TOTAL	748[r]	739[r]	728[r]	751[r]	688
Four-Engine—TOTAL	15	18	19	17	19
Douglas DC-6	15	18	19	17	19
Three-Engine—TOTAL	1	7	4	3	3
Pilatus Britten-Norman BN2A-MK-3 Turbo Islander	1	7	4	3	3
Twin-Engine—TOTAL	333[r]	317[r]	298[r]	391[r]	292
Single-Engine—TOTAL	399	397	407	340	374
Helicopters—TOTAL	118	121	134	117	122

Source: Federal Aviation Administration, "FAA Statistical Handbook of Aviation" (Annually).
NOTE: Effective 1978, includes certificated route air carriers, supplemental air carriers (charters), multi-engine aircraft in passenger service of commuters, and all aircraft over 12,500 pounds operated by Part 121 and Part 135 commuter operators.
a   "Active aircraft" equals the average number of aircraft reported in operation during the last quarter of the year.
r   Revised.

JET FUEL COSTS AND CONSUMPTION BY U.S. AIR CARRIERS[a]
Calendar Years 1978–1999

Year	Gallons Consumed (Millions)	Total Cost (Millions)	Cost Per Gallon (Cents)	Cost Index (1982 = 100)	Cost of Fuel as Percent of Cash Operating Expenses
1978	10,359.5	$ 4,069.6	39.3 ¢	39.0	19.4%
1979	11,042.0	6,354.0	57.5	57.1	24.3
1980	10,854.0	9,818.3	90.5	89.7	30.0
1981	10,326.9	10,827.5	104.8	104.0	29.9
1982	9,942.5	10,024.6	100.8	100.0	27.5
1983	10,472.5	9,320.9	89.0	88.3	24.7
1984	11,424.0	9,740.2	85.3	84.6	24.0
1985	12,072.6	9,689.8	80.3	79.6	22.3
1986	13,006.9	7,275.8	55.9	55.5	15.5
1987	14,139.6	7,895.6	55.8	55.4	15.0
1988	14,871.4	7,943.5	53.4	53.0	13.5
1989	15,115.8	9,104.3	60.2	59.7	13.9
1990	15,945.9	12,405.9	77.8	77.2	17.3
1991	14,682.9	10,275.2	70.0	69.4	14.5
1992	15,413.1	10,095.5	65.5	65.0	13.5
1993	15,569.3	9,378.7	60.2	59.7	12.4
1994	16,041.3	8,798.5	54.8	54.4	11.6[r]
1995	16,233.1	9,053.2	55.8	55.3	12.0[r]
1996	16,848.4	10,979.4	65.2	64.6	13.0
1997	17,450.8	10,990.1	63.0	62.5	12.5
1998	17,923.1	8,924.9	49.8	49.4	9.9
1999	18,693.9	9,534.8	51.0	50.6	9.9

Source: Air Transport Association of America, "Airline Cost Index" (Quarterly).
   a   Majors and Nationals.
   r   Revised.

U.S. CIVIL AND JOINT-USE AIRCRAFT FACILITIES[a]
BY TYPE AND STATE
As of December 31, 1999

State	TOTAL[a]	Public[b]	Paved	Lighted	State	TOTAL[a]	Public[b]	Paved	Lighted
Alabama.........	256	97	156	102	Nevada	121	51	61	34
Alaska............	584	407	73	172	New Hampshire	107	27	50	21
Arizona	295	78	166	83	New Jersey	368	53	156	52
Arkansas.........	288	101	178	102	New Mexico......	171	66	82	54
California	947	265	671	273	New York	570	166	218	145
Colorado	414	80	177	86	North Carolina ...	388	114	161	119
Connecticut ...	149	24	91	29	North Dakota ...	437	92	84	93
Delaware	41	11	17	13	Ohio	747	176	291	179
Dist. of Col. ...	16	3	15	4	Oklahoma.........	433	150	217	131
Florida	832	129	353	170	Oregon	421	100	157	76
Georgia	433	110	193	117	Pennsylvania......	783	146	321	139
Hawaii	46	12	37	15	Rhode Island......	26	8	20	8
Idaho	228	120	79	49	South Carolina ...	177	67	84	73
Illinois............	924	122	299	166	South Dakota ...	175	74	75	73
Indiana	618	114	170	117	Tennessee	279	82	152	89
Iowa	313	122	174	134	Texas	1,761	385	843	432
Kansas	405	143	143	128	Utah	135	46	88	48
Kentucky	194	63	115	63	Vermont...........	81	17	19	11
Louisiana	461	84	244	78	Virginia	398	66	162	88
Maine............	160	65	54	34	Washington	460	138	224	133
Maryland	221	36	84	48	West Virginia ...	115	40	69	35
Massachusetts	221	46	118	42	Wisconsin	529	134	187	145
Michigan	484	233	203	184	Wyoming	111	41	57	41
Minnesota	502	158	159	143	**50 States—Total**	19,158	5,295	8,329	4,978
Mississippi	240	83	120	85	Puerto Rico	36	11	32	10
Missouri	532	135	234	142	Virgin Islands ...	9	2	3	2
Montana.........	256	122	108	90	S. Pacific[c]	17	9	11	6
Nebraska	305	93	120	90	**TOTAL**	19,220	5,317	8,375	4,996

FACILITIES BY CLASS

Class	Total[a]	Public[b]	Private
Airports	13,642	5,040	8,602
Heliports	5,021	79	4,942
Stolports	88	4	84
Seaplane Bases	469	194	275
Total Facilities	19,220	5,317	13,903

Source: Federal Aviation Administration, "FAA Statistical Handbook of Aviation" (Annually).
   a   Included in these data are facilities having joint civil-military use.
   b   "Public" refers to use, whether publicly or privately owned.
   c   American Samoa, Guam, and Trust Territories.

HELIPORTS/HELIPADS[a] IN THE UNITED STATES
BY STATE
As of 1999

State	Total Helipads in State	Private Use		Public Use	
		Heliports & Helistops	Helipads at Airports	Heliports & Helistops	Helipads at Airports
Alabama	72	71	—	—	1
Alaska	29	19	1	6	3
Arizona	104	98	1	—	5
Arkansas	82	79	1	—	2
California	401	380	2	—	19
Colorado	168	163	—	—	5
Connecticut	85	80	—	2	3
Delaware	14	12	—	1	1
District of Columbia	19	18	—	1	—
Florida	264	261	1	1	1
Georgia	99	97	—	—	2
Hawaii	18	16	—	—	2
Idaho	35	33	1	—	1
Illinois	252	242	3	7	—
Indiana	117	111	3	2	1
Iowa	84	83	—	—	1
Kansas	38	34	—	—	4
Kentucky	47	47	—	—	—
Louisiana	232	224	2	4	2
Maine	16	15	—	—	1
Maryland	62	60	1	—	1
Massachusetts	129	125	—	2	2
Michigan	87	84	1	2	—
Minnesota	47	45	—	—	2
Mississippi	46	46	—	—	—
Missouri	125	122	1	2	—
Montana	28	25	—	2	1
Nebraska	33	31	1	—	1
Nevada	27	25	—	—	2
New Hampshire	46	45	—	—	1

(Continued on next page)

HELIPORTS/HELIPADS[a] IN THE UNITED STATES
BY STATE (Continued)
As of 1999

State	Total Helipads in State	Private Use		Public Use	
		Heliports & Helistops	Helipads at Airports	Heliports & Helistops	Helipads at Airports
New Jersey	247	241	—	3	3
New Mexico	24	22	1	1	—
New York	144	131	—	8	5
North Carolina	69	66	—	3	—
North Dakota	17	16	—	—	1
Ohio	208	190	1	14	3
Oklahoma	93	87	—	5	1
Oregon	96	92	2	2	—
Pennsylvania	308	299	1	6	2
Rhode Island	16	15	—	1	—
South Carolina	25	23	—	—	2
South Dakota	25	25	—	—	—
Tennessee	82	79	1	1	1
Texas	425	410	3	6	6
Utah	42	40	—	—	2
Vermont	18	18	—	—	—
Virginia	122	118	—	—	4
Washington	134	124	3	1	6
West Virginia	36	33	—	—	3
Wisconsin	81	80	—	—	1
Wyoming	20	18	—	—	2
Total U.S.	5,038	4,818	31	83	106

Source: Helicopter Association International, "2000 Helicopter Annual" (Annually).
NOTE: 96.2 percent of all U.S. helicopter landing areas are private, while 3.8 percent are public.
  a Excludes temporary heliports, offshore heliports, and infrequently used helicopter landing sites.

ACTIVE U.S. CIVIL AIRCRAFT[a]
As of December 31, 1964–1998
(in thousands)

Year	TOTAL	Air Carrier[b]	General Aviation Aircraft					
				Fixed-Wing Aircraft				
			TOTAL	Multi-Engine	Single-Engine		Rotor-craft[c]	Other[d]
					4-place & over	3-place & less		
1964	90.8	2.057	88.7	10.6	45.8	30.4	1.3	0.6
1965	97.6	2.125	95.4	12.0	49.8	31.4	1.5	0.8
1966	107.0	2.272	104.7	13.5	53.0	35.7	1.6	0.9
1967	116.6	2.452	114.2	14.7	56.9	39.7	1.9	1.1
1968	126.8	2.586	124.2	16.8	61.0	42.8	2.4	1.3
1969	133.5	2.690	130.8	18.1	63.7	45.0	2.6	1.4
1970	134.4	2.679	131.7	18.3	64.8	44.9	2.3	1.6
1971	133.8	2.642	131.1	17.9	64.5	44.8	2.4	1.7
1972	147.6	2.583	145.0	19.8	71.0	49.4	2.8	1.9
1973	156.1	2.599	153.5	21.9	74.8	51.4	3.1	2.3
1974	164.0	2.472	161.5	23.4	78.9	53.0	3.6	2.5
1975	171.0	2.495	168.5	24.6	82.6	54.4	4.1	2.8
1976	180.8	2.492	178.3	25.7	88.2	56.7	4.5	3.2
1977	186.8	2.473	184.3	26.7	92.0	57.3	4.7	3.6
1978	201.3	2.545	198.8	28.8	101.5	59.2	5.3	4.0
1979	213.9	3.609	210.3	31.3	106.0	62.4	5.9	4.8
1980	214.9	3.808	211.0	31.7	107.9	60.5	6.0	4.9
1981	217.2	3.973	213.2	33.3	108.0	59.9	7.0	5.0
1982	213.9	4.027	209.8	34.2	106.5	57.7	6.2	6.2
1983	217.5	4.203	213.3	34.6	107.1	59.1	6.5	5.9
1984	225.3	4.370	220.9	35.6	109.9	62.0	7.1	6.3
1985	201.2	4.678	196.5	31.3	98.5	54.9	6.0	5.8
1986	210.2	4.909	205.3	32.0	102.0	58.3	6.5	6.5
1987	208.0	5.253	202.7	30.8	100.4	59.3	5.9	6.3
1988	201.9	5.660	196.2	30.1	98.1	55.6	6.0	6.4
1989	210.8	5.778	205.0	31.9	100.5	58.4	7.0	7.2
1990	204.1	6.083	198.0	30.6[r]	97.6	56.4	6.9	6.6
1991	202.9	6.054	196.9	29.7	97.8	55.1	6.2	8.1
1992	193.0	7.320	185.7	26.8	91.6	53.2	6.0	8.0
1993	184.4	7.297	177.1	22.8	91.6	42.5	4.7	15.5
1994	180.3	7.370	172.9	22.3	87.3	40.5	4.7	18.1
1995	190.0	7.411	188.1	24.6	93.6	44.1	5.8	19.9
1996	194.8	7.478	191.1	25.6	93.8	44.3	6.6	20.9
1997	200.0	7.616	192.4	26.2	95.0	45.7	6.8	18.8
1998	212.8	8.111	204.7	31.0	102.5	41.8	7.4	22.1

Source: Federal Aviation Administration, "FAA Statistical Handbook of Aviation" (Annually).
 a "Active aircraft" must have a current U.S. registration and have flown during the calendar year. Prior to 1971, only a current U.S. registration was necessary.
 b Effective 1978, includes certificated route air carriers, supplemental air carriers (charters), multi-engine aircraft in commuter passenger service, and all aircraft over 12,500 pounds operated by air taxis, commercial operators, and travel clubs.
 c Includes autogiros; excludes air carrier helicopters.
 d Includes gliders, dirigibles, balloons, and experimental aircraft.

ACTIVE U.S. CIVIL AIRCRAFT
BY PRIMARY USE AND TYPE OF AIRCRAFT
As of December 31, 1998

Primary Use[a]	TOTAL	Fixed-Wing			Rotor-craft[b]	Other[c]
		Turbojet	Turboprop	Piston		
TOTAL—ALL AIRCRAFT ...	212,821	11,477	8,006	163,714	7,542	22,082
Air Carrier—TOTAL	8,111	5,411	1,832	751	117	—
Large	7,161	5,396	1,695	70	—	—
Small	950	15	137	681	117	—
General Aviation—TOTAL	204,710	6,066	6,174	162,963	7,425	22,082
Executive........................	11,250	4,701	2,448	3,392	494	215
Business	32,611	228	1,502	29,513	443	924
Air Taxi[d]	4,878	515	959	2,351	1,030	22
Instructional	11,375	—	13	10,301	608	454
Personal	124,347	198	345	105,066	1,094	17,643
Aerial Application	4,550	81	342	3,438	590	99
Aerial Observation...........	3,242	—	20	2,496	586	141
Sight Seeing	679	—	—	192	155	332
Air Tours	312	—	—	185	127	—
External Load	313	—	—	8	282	23
Public Use	4,029	210	335	1,669	1,723	92
Other Work	1,116	12	26	988	27	63
Other	6,010	119	184	3,366	266	2,075

Source: Federal Aviation Administration, "FAA Statistical Handbook of Aviation" (Annually) and General Aviation Manufacturers Association, "General Aviation Statistical Databook" (Annually).

NOTE: Detail may not add to totals because of estimating procedures.

a   Definitions of "primary use" categories available in Glossary of "FAA Statistical Handbook."
b   Includes helicopters and autogiros.
c   Includes gliders, dirigibles, and balloons.
d   Limited to Air taxis under 12,500 pounds. Otherwise, aircraft included in "Air Carrier."

U.S. GENERAL AVIATION[a]
TYPE OF AIRCRAFT AND HOURS FLOWN
Calendar Years 1994–1998

	1994	1995	1996	1997	1998
Number of Active Aircraft by Type (in thousands)					
All Aircraft—TOTAL	172.9	188.1	191.1	192.4	204.7
Fixed-Wing:	150.2	162.3	163.7	166.9	175.2
Piston:	142.2	152.8	153.6	156.1	163.0
Single-Engine	127.4	137.0	137.4	140.0	144.2
Twin-Engine	14.8	15.7	16.1	15.9	18.7
Other	0.1	0.0	0.1	0.1	0.1
Turboprop:	4.1	5.0	5.7	5.6	6.2
Twin-Engine	3.6	4.3	4.9	4.9	5.1
Other	0.5	0.7	0.8	0.7	1.1
Turbojet:	3.9	4.6	4.4	5.2	6.1
Twin-Engine	3.7	4.1	4.1	4.6	5.5
Other	0.3	0.5	0.3	0.5	0.6
Rotorcraft:	4.7	5.8	6.6	6.8	7.4
Piston	1.6	1.9	2.5	2.3	2.5
Turbine	3.1	4.0	4.1	4.5	4.9
Balloons, Dirigibles, and Gliders...	5.9	4.7	4.2	4.1	5.6
Experimental	12.1	15.2	16.6	14.7	16.5
Hours Flown by Type of Aircraft (in thousands)					
All Aircraft—TOTAL	24,092	26,612	26,909	27,713	28,100
Fixed-Wing: Piston	18,823	20,251	20,091	20,743	20,402
Turboprop	1,142	1,490	1,768	1,655	1,765
Turbojet	1,238	1,455	1,543	1,713	2,226
Rotorcraft: Piston	369	337	591	343	430
Turbine	1,408	1,624	1,531	1,739	1,912
Balloons, Dirigibles, and Gliders...	388	261	227	192	295
Experimental	724	1,194	1,158	1,327	1,071
Average Hours Flown Annually by Type					
All Aircraft—TOTAL	139.3	141.5	140.8	144.0	137.3
Fixed-Wing: Piston	132.4	132.5	130.8	132.9	125.2
Turboprop	279.0	298.3	309.3	294.5	285.8
Turbojet	316.3	319.1	348.7	330.7	367.0
Rotorcraft: Piston	226.6	181.0	235.9	152.2	169.0
Turbine	454.1	409.3	376.9	384.3	391.8
Balloons, Dirigibles, and Gliders...	65.8	55.1	53.6	46.8	52.8
Experimental	59.6	78.7	69.6	90.4	64.9

Source: Federal Aviation Administration, "FAA Statistical Handbook of Aviation" (Annually) and the Federal Aviation Administration, Office of Management Systems.
NOTE: Detail may not add to totals because of rounding and/or estimating procedures.
   a Beginning in 1993, commuters were excluded from the survey.
   NA Not available.

U.S. GENERAL AVIATION
ACTIVE AIRCRAFT AND HOURS FLOWN
BY PRIMARY USE
Calendar Years 1994–1998

Primary Use[a]	1994	1995	1996	1997	1998
ACTIVE AIRCRAFT AS OF DECEMBER 31 (in thousands)					
TOTAL......................	176.6	188.1	191.1	192.4	204.7
Executive.....................	10.2	10.6	9.9	10.4	11.3
Business	26.5	28.3	30.7	27.7	32.6
Air Taxi[b]	4.2	3.8	4.1	4.8	4.9
Instructional	15.1	14.2	12.7	14.7	11.4
Personal	104.1	113.4	113.4	115.6	124.3
Aerial Application	4.4	5.0	5.0	4.9	4.6
Aerial Observation.........	5.1	4.7	3.0	3.3	3.2
Sight Seeing	1.3	0.8	0.7	0.7	0.7
Public Use	NA	NA	4.5	4.1	4.0
Air Tours	NA	0.2	0.1	0.2	0.3
External Load	0.1	0.2	0.4	0.2	0.3
Other Work	1.2	1.1	1.0	0.7	1.1
Other	4.4	5.9	5.6	5.3	6.0
HOURS FLOWN (in thousands)					
TOTAL......................	24,092	26,612	26,909	27,713	28,100
Executive...................	2,486	3,069	2,898	2,878	3,213
Business	3,012	3,335	3,259	3,006	3,523
Air Taxi[b]	1,545	1,403	1,734	2,008	2,400
Instructional	4,382	4,410	4,759	4,956	3,961
Personal	8,248	9,659	9,037	9,644	9,781
Aerial Application	1,364	1,526	1,713	1,562	1,306
Aerial Observation.........	1,746	1,391	1,057	1,261	812
Sight Seeing	309	179	195	127	169
Air Tours	NA	124	100	114	183
Public Use	NA	NA	1,047	1,096	1,373
External Load	135	128	191	112	153
Other Work	241	280	265	139	286
Other	622	1,107	656	819	940

Source: Federal Aviation Administration, "FAA Statistical Handbook of Aviation" (Annually).
NOTE: Detail may not add to totals because of rounding and estimating procedures.
  a Definitions of "primary use" categories available in Glossary of "FAA Statistical Handbook."
  b Air taxis under 12,500 pounds.
  NA Not available.

FEDERAL OUTLAYS FOR R&D ROSE $2.3 BILLION TO AN ESTI-mated $76 billion in FY 2000. While current dollar R&D outlays at DoD rose slightly to $38 billion, they declined at NASA to $9.2 billion. After adjusting for inflation, outlays at both agencies declined in real terms from the previous year—down 1% at DoD and 3% at NASA, respectively.

For FY 2001, OMB projects an increase of $3.9 billion to $80 billion in federal outlays for R&D. NASA's R&D spending is projected to rise 1% to $9.3 billion, while DoD rises only slightly to $38 billion. Again, inflation-adjusted R&D spending at NASA and DoD is estimated to decline in real terms in FY 2001.

R&D funding from all sources for all purposes in 1999 rose $18 billion to $245 billion, according to NSF's annual survey. Two-thirds of the total was funded by industry—up $14 billion to $162 billion. Federal funding (28% of the total) rose 4.5% to $69 billion. The remaining sources (local government, colleges and universities,

and nonprofit institutions) provided 5% of total national R&D funding.

Industry performed three-quarters, or $184 billion, of the total R&D performed in the United States in 1999. Colleges and universities conducted 11.5% and federal government labs accounted for 7.4%. While FFRDC's R&D rose just 1.4% to $5.6 billion, R&D performed by nonprofit institutions rose 7.9% to $8.4 billion.

For 2000, NSF estimates that total R&D funding will increase 8% to $264 billion and that industry will again be the principal performer (76%) and the principal funding source (68%). Federal government R&D funding is expected to increase $1.7 billion to $71 billion. R&D performed at colleges and universities will rise $1.8 billion to $30 billion; and college and university self-funding of R&D will increase $0.4 billion to $5.8 billion.

In 1998, aerospace industry-performed R&D decreased 11% to $14.4 billion. Federal funding declined 12% to $9.3 billion; and company funding declined 10% to $5.1 billion. When expressed as a percentage of sales, company-funded aerospace R&D fell to an eight-year low of 3.3%. Still, the aerospace industry continues to invest a higher percentage of its sales in R&D than the overall average for the manufacturing sector.

In FY 1999, DoD prime contract awards for RDT&E totaled $19.4 billion, down from $20.1 billion in the previous year. RDT&E contract awards for missile and space systems exceeded aircraft RDT&E for the third consecutive year. Missile/space RDT&E declined

9% to $4.8 billion in FY 1999. Aircraft RDT&E also declined 11% to $4.1 billion. Electronics and communications equipment RDT&E grew 7% to $3.2 billion. All other categories combined rose just 1.3% to $7.4 billion in FY 1999.

In a geographical breakdown of FY 1999 DoD awards for RDT&E to business firms, the South Atlantic region topped the list for the sixth straight year, with contracts totaling $5.4 billion. In second place was the Pacific region ($4.0 billion), followed by the Mountain ($1.9 billion) and East South Central ($1.4 billion) regions.

TOTAL U.S. FUNDS FOR RESEARCH AND DEVELOPMENT
BY SOURCE AND PERFORMER[a]
Calendar Years 1997–2000
(Millions of Dollars)

Source of Funds	TOTAL, All Performers	Performer				
		Federal Government	Industry	Colleges & Universities	Federally-Funded Research & Development Centers	Non-Profit Institutions
1997[r]						
All Sources—TOTAL	$212,192	$16,817	$157,539	$24,962	$5,486	$7,38(
Federal Government	64,756	16,817	23,928	14,749	5,486	3,77?
Gov't, Non-Federal	1,906	—	—	1,906	—	—
Industry	136,205	—	133,611	1,785	—	80(
Colleges & Universities ...	4,747	—	—	4,747	—	—
Nonprofit Institutions......	4,579	—	—	1,776	—	2,80(
1998[r]						
All Sources—TOTAL	$226,515	$17,403	$169,180	$26,547	$5,570	$7,81(
Federal Government	66,522	17,403	24,164	15,533	5,570	3,85?
Gov't, Non-Federal	1,993	—	—	1,993	—	—
Industry	147,829	—	145,016	1,933	—	88(
Colleges & Universities ...	5,166	—	—	5,166	—	—
Nonprofit Institutions......	5,006	—	—	1,923	—	3,08?
1999[p]						
All Sources—TOTAL	$244,828	$18,114	$184,379	$28,255	$5,649	$8,43?
Federal Government	69,494	18,114	25,138	16,457	5,649	4,13(
Gov't, Non-Federal	2,143	—	—	2,143	—	—
Industry	162,280	—	159,241	2,070	—	96(
Colleges & Universities ...	5,534	—	—	5,534	—	—
Nonprofit Institutions......	5,376	—	—	2,050	—	3,32(
2000[E]						
All Sources—TOTAL	$264,165	$17,777	$201,722	$30,090	$5,727	$8,84(
Federal Government	71,162	17,777	26,060	17,408	5,727	4,19(
Gov't, Non-Federal	2,322	—	—	2,322	—	—
Industry	178,959	—	175,662	2,224	—	1,07?
Colleges & Universities ...	5,951	—	—	5,951	—	—
Nonprofit Institutions......	5,770	—	—	2,184	—	3,58(

Source: National Science Foundation, "Annual Survey of Industrial Research and Development" (Annually).
a Source/performer detail not available by industry.
E Estimate.
p Preliminary.
r Revised.

FUNDS FOR INDUSTRIAL RESEARCH AND DEVELOPMENT
ALL INDUSTRIES AND THE AEROSPACE INDUSTRY
By Funding Source
Calendar Years 1984–1998
(Millions of Dollars)

Year	All Industries[a]			Aerospace Industry[b]		
	Total	Federal Funds	Company Funds[c]	Total	Federal Funds	Company Funds[c]
CURRENT DOLLARS						
1984	$ 74,800	$23,396	$ 51,404	$18,858	$14,094	$4,764
1985	84,239	27,196	57,043	22,231	16,582	5,649
1986	87,823	27,891	59,932	21,050	14,984	6,066
1987	92,155	30,752	61,403	24,458	18,519	5,939
1988	97,015	30,343	66,672	24,168	18,402	5,766
1989	102,055	28,554	73,501	22,331	16,828	5,503
1990	109,727	28,125	81,602	20,635	15,248	5,387
1991	116,952	26,372	90,580	16,629	11,096	5,533
1992	119,110	24,722	94,388	17,158	10,287	6,871
1993	117,400	22,809	94,591	15,056	9,372	5,684
1994	119,595	22,463	97,131	14,260	8,794	5,466
1995	132,103	23,451	108,652	16,951	11,462	5,489
1996	144,667	23,653	121,015	16,224	10,515	5,710
1997	157,539	23,928	133,611	16,296	10,619	5,677
1998	169,180	24,164	145,016	14,449	9,341	5,108
CONSTANT DOLLARS[dr]						
1984	$104,762	$32,768	$ 71,994	$26,412	$19,739	$6,672
1985	114,300	36,901	77,399	30,164	22,499	7,665
1986	116,631	37,040	79,591	27,955	19,899	8,056
1987	118,756	39,629	79,128	31,518	23,865	7,653
1988	120,966	37,834	83,132	30,135	22,945	7,190
1989	122,515	34,279	88,236	26,808	20,202	6,606
1990	126,852	32,514	94,338	23,855	17,628	6,228
1991	130,381	29,400	100,981	18,538	12,370	6,168
1992	129,749	26,930	102,819	18,691	11,206	7,485
1993	124,761	24,239	100,522	16,000	9,960	6,040
1994	124,578	23,399	101,178	14,854	9,160	5,694
1995	134,662	23,905	110,756	17,279	11,684	5,595
1996	144,667	23,653	121,015	16,224	10,515	5,710
1997	154,602	23,482	131,120	15,992	10,421	5,571
1998	164,093	23,437	140,656	14,015	9,060	4,954

Source: National Science Foundation, "Annual Survey of Industrial Research and Development" (Annually).
NOTE: Detail may not add to totals because of rounding.
a Includes all manufacturing industries, plus those non-manufacturing industries known to conduct or finance research and development.
b Companies classified in SIC codes 372 and 376, having as their principal activity the manufacture of aircraft, guided missiles, space vehicles, and parts.
c Company funds include all funds for industrial R&D work performed within company facilities except funds provided by the Federal Government. Excluded are company-financed research and development contracted to outside organizations such as research institutions, universities and colleges, or other non-profit organizations.
d Based on GDP deflator, 1996=100.
r Revised.

FUNDS FOR INDUSTRIAL RESEARCH AND DEVELOPMENT IN THE AEROSPACE INDUSTRY

By Type of Research and Funding Source
Calendar Years 1964–1998
(Millions of Dollars)

Year	TOTAL AERO-SPACE	Basic Research			Applied Research			Development		
		Total	Federal Funds	Company Funds	Total	Federal Funds	Company Funds	Total	Federal Funds	Company Funds
1964	$ 5,078	$ 67	$ 34	$ 28	$ 766	$ 607	$ 159	$ 4,244	$ 3,948	$ 296
1965	5,148	71	41	30	735	563	172	4,342	3,921	421
1966	5,526	69	36	33	773	563	210	4,685	4,162	523
1967	5,669	71	33	38	726	490	236	4,871	4,071	800
1968	5,765	68	26	42	677	426	251	5,021	4,145	876
1969	5,882	65	24	41	597	347	250	5,220	4,216	1,004
1970	5,219	63	20	43	565	352	213	4,591	3,718	873
1971	4,881	54	37	17	461	279	182	4,365	3,583	782
1972	4,950	60	44	16	451	267	184	4,438	3,722	716
1973	5,052	50	21	29	512	308	204	4,491	3,633	858
1974	5,278	51	19	32	609	360	249	4,617	3,735	882
1975	5,713	54	17	37	614	381	233	5,044	4,119	925
1976	6,339	54	21	33	666	365	301	5,619	4,521	1,098
1977	7,033	56	25	31	753	419	334	6,223	5,017	1,206
1979[a]	8,041	86	44	42	880	499	381	7,076	5,314	1,762
1981[a]	11,968	131	60	71	1,484	897	587	10,353	7,738	2,615
1983	13,853	146	NA	NA	3,466	NA	NA	10,241	7,668	2,573
1984	16,033	247	NA	NA	3,067	NA	NA	12,718	9,870	2,848
1985	17,619	304	162	142	3,785	2,776	1,009	13,530	10,483	3,047
1986	21,050	311	208	103	3,198	1,571	1,627	17,541	13,205	4,336
1987	24,488	425	335	90	2,949	1,709	1,239	21,115	16,475	4,640
1988	25,900	366	263	104	2,997	1,915	1,082	22,537	17,700	4,838
1989	25,638	668	553	116	3,081	2,113	968	21,889	16,967	4,921
1990	25,356	658	519	139	3,340	1,931	1,409	21,358	16,766	4,592
1991	16,983	364	302	62	2,091	1,105	986	14,528	10,043 [b]	4,485
1992	17,158	270	235	35	1,739	976	763	15,148	9,076	6,072
1993	15,056	NA	NA	NA	1,453	825	628	NA	NA	NA
1994	14,260	NA	NA	NA	NA	NA	NA	12,787	7,978	4,809
1995	16,951	252	250	2	1,987	564	1,423	14,712	10,648	4,064
1996	16,224	NA	NA	108	NA	NA	NA	13,259	9,264	3,995
1997	16,296	NA	NA	10	NA	NA	1,508	13,275	9,115	4,159
1998	14,449	NA	NA	172	NA	NA	272	12,800	8,136	4,664

Source: National Science Foundation, "Annual Survey of Industrial Research and Development" (Annually).
NOTE: Detail may not add to totals because of rounding.
    a Break-outs by Research Type and Funding Source available only for odd-numbered years between 1977 and 1983.
    b Computed by AIA as difference between total and company funds. Figure withheld by NSF because of imputation of more than 50 percent.
NA Not available.

RESEARCH AND DEVELOPMENT FUNDS AS PERCENT OF NET SALES
ALL MANUFACTURING INDUSTRIES AND THE AEROSPACE INDUSTRY
Calendar Years 1978–1998

Year	All Manufacturing Industries[a]		Aerospace Industry[b]	
	Total Funds	Company Funds	Total Funds	Company Funds
1978	2.9%	2.0%	13.3%	3.2%
1979	2.6	1.9	12.9	3.5
1980	3.0	2.1	13.7	3.8
1981	3.1	2.2	16.0	4.6
1982	3.8	2.6	17.1	5.1
1983	3.9	2.6	15.2	4.1
1984	3.9	2.6	15.4	4.0
1985	4.4	3.0	14.9	3.9
1986	4.7	3.2	13.4	4.0
1987	4.6	3.1	14.7	3.6
1988	4.5	3.1	16.3	3.9
1989	4.3	3.1	13.5	3.3
1990	4.2	3.1	11.8	3.1
1991	4.2	3.2	12.1	4.0
1992	4.2	3.3	11.8	4.7
1993	3.8	3.1	12.5	4.7
1994	3.6	2.9	13.8	5.3
1995	3.6	2.9	12.9	4.2
1996	4.0	3.3	12.9	4.5
1997	3.9	3.3	11.2	3.9
1998	3.7	3.2	9.3	3.3

Source: National Science Foundation, "Annual Survey of Industrial Research and Development" (Annually).
a Includes all manufacturing industries known to conduct or finance research and development.
b Companies classified in SIC codes 372 and 376, having as their principal activity the manufacture of aircraft, guided missiles, space vehicles, and parts.

FEDERAL OUTLAYS FOR CONDUCT OF
RESEARCH AND DEVELOPMENT
Fiscal Years 1987–2001
(Millions of Dollars)

Year	TOTAL	DoD	NASA	Energy[a]	Other[b]
CURRENT DOLLARS					
1987	$53,256	$34,732	$3,250	$5,262	$10,012
1988	56,100	35,605	3,832	5,332	11,331
1989	60,760	37,819	4,975	5,681	12,285
1990	63,810	38,247	6,325	5,957	13,281
1991	62,183	35,330	7,072	5,892	13,889
1992	64,728	35,504	7,617	6,043	15,564
1993	68,378	37,666	8,088	6,036	16,588
1994	68,453	35,474	7,878	5,904	19,197
1995	68,432	35,356	8,992	6,195	17,889
1996	68,439	36,936	8,083	6,135	17,285
1997	71,073	37,702	9,374	5,819	18,178
1998	72,803	37,558	9,881	5,971	19,393
1999	74,136	37,571	9,433	6,077	21,055
2000[E]	76,463	37,619	9,238	6,420	23,186
2001[E]	80,361	37,805	9,329	7,012	26,215
CONSTANT DOLLARS[cr]					
1987	$68,895	$44,931	$4,204	$6,807	$12,952
1988	70,213	44,562	4,796	6,673	14,181
1989	73,293	45,620	6,001	6,853	14,819
1990	74,198	44,473	7,355	6,927	15,443
1991	69,556	39,519	7,911	6,591	15,536
1992	70,587	38,718	8,306	6,590	16,973
1993	72,820	40,113	8,613	6,428	17,666
1994	71,305	36,952	8,206	6,150	19,997
1995	69,829	36,078	9,176	6,321	18,254
1996	68,439	36,936	8,083	6,135	17,285
1997	69,748	36,999	9,199	5,711	17,839
1998	70,477	36,358	9,565	5,780	18,773
1999	70,876	35,919	9,018	5,810	20,129
2000[E]	72,203	35,523	8,723	6,062	21,894
2001[E]	74,408	35,005	8,638	6,493	24,273

Source: Office of Management and Budget, "The Budget of the United States Government" (Annually).
NOTE: Detail may not add to totals because of rounding.
a Includes defense and nondefense-related atomic energy R&D with nondefense energy R&D.
b Includes but not limited to NSF, NIH, DoT, & Agriculture.
c Based on Fiscal Year GDP deflator, 1996=100.
E Estimate. Latest year reflects Administration's budget proposal.
r Revised.

FEDERAL AERONAUTICS RESEARCH AND DEVELOPMENT
Fiscal Years 1983–1999
(Millions of Dollars)

Year	TOTAL	NASA[a]	DoD[b]	DoT[c]
BUDGET AUTHORITY				
1983	$ 3,871	$ 547	$3,221	$ 103
1984	4,087	600	3,224	263
1985	4,335	648	3,422	265
1986	6,660	601	4,927	1,132
1987	5,824	698	4,179	946
1988	6,974	723	4,989	1,262
1989	10,656	872	8,240	1,544
1990	10,690	932	7,867	1,891
1991	9,417	968	6,149	2,300
1992	11,110	1,117	7,366	2,627
1993	11,359	1,245	7,582	2,532
1994	10,703	1,546	6,848	2,309
1995	10,718	1,310	7,196	2,212
1996	10,159	1,315	6,792	2,052
1997	9,721	1,252	6,323	2,146
1998	9,610	1,327	6,184	2,099
1999[E]	8,882	1,194	5,417	2,271
OUTLAYS				
1983	$ 3,817	$ 563	$2,920	$ 334
1984	4,005	586	2,995	424
1985	4,435	643	3,101	691
1986	6,073	648	4,373	1,052
1987	5,867	622	4,182	1,063
1988	6,340	679	4,448	1,213
1989	8,491	855	6,420	1,216
1990	10,009	889	7,649	1,471
1991	9,501	1,017	6,793	1,691
1992	10,011	1,122	6,790	2,099
1993	11,162	1,212	7,572	2,378
1994	11,137	1,330	7,203	2,604
1995	11,155	1,153	7,132	2,870
1996	10,837	1,187	6,974	2,676
1997	10,430	1,302	6,600	2,528
1998	10,086	1,339	6,318	2,429
1999[E]	9,414	1,218	5,827	2,369

Source: NASA, "Aeronautics and Space Report of the President" (Annually).
a Research and Development, Construction of Facilities, Research and Program Management.
b Research, Development, Test, and Evaluation of aircraft and related equipment.
c Federal Aviation Administration: Research, Engineering, and Development; and Facilities, Engineering, and Development.
E Estimate.

DEPARTMENT OF DEFENSE
OUTLAYS FOR RESEARCH, DEVELOPMENT, TEST, AND EVALUATION
Fiscal Years 1972–2001
(Millions of Dollars)

Year	TOTAL, All RDT&E Functions	Air Force	Navy	Army	Other
1972	$ 7,881	$ 3,205	$2,427	$1,779	$ 470
1973	8,157	3,362	2,404	1,912	479
1974	8,582	3,240	2,623	2,190	529
1975	8,866	3,308	3,021	1,964	573
1976	8,923	3,338	3,215	1,842	528
Tr.Qtr.	2,203	830	778	437	161
1977	9,795	3,618	3,481	2,069	627
1978	10,508	3,626	3,825	2,342	715
1979	11,152	4,080	3,826	2,409	837
1980	13,127	5,017	4,381	2,707	1,021
1981	15,278	6,341	4,783	2,958	1,196
1982	17,729	7,794	5,240	3,230	1,465
1983	20,554	9,182	5,854	3,658	1,861
1984	23,117	10,353	6,662	3,812	2,289
1985	27,103	11,573	8,054	3,950	3,527
1986	32,283	13,417	9,667	3,984	5,215
1987	33,596	13,347	9,176	4,721	6,352
1988	34,792	14,302	8,828	4,624	7,038
1989	37,002	14,912	9,291	4,966	7,833
1990	37,458	14,443	9,160	5,513	8,342
1991	34,589	13,050	7,586	5,559	8,371
1992	34,632	11,998	7,826	5,978	8,830
1993	36,968	12,338	8,944	6,218	9,467
1994	34,786	12,513	7,990	5,746	8,537
1995	34,710	12,052	9,230	5,081	8,347
1996	36,561	13,056	9,404	4,925	9,175
1997	37,027	14,040	8,220	4,859	9,908
1998	37,420	14,499	7,836	4,881	10,204
1999	37,363	14,172	8,052	5,027	10,112
2000 [E]	37,400	13,451	9,074	5,039	9,836
2001 [E]	37,696	13,554	8,717	5,251	10,174

Source: Office of Management and Budget, "The Budget of the United States Government" (Annually).
E Estimate. Latest year reflects Administration's budget proposal.
Tr.Qtr. See Glossary.

DEPARTMENT OF DEFENSE
APPROPRIATIONS FOR
RESEARCH, DEVELOPMENT, TEST, AND EVALUATION
Fiscal Years 1999–2001
(Millions of Dollars)

	1999	2000^E	2001^E
TOTAL—APPROPRIATIONS FOR RDT&E	$38,104	$38,289	$37,862

BY APPROPRIATION

	1999	2000^E	2001^E
Army	$ 5,031	$ 5,225	$ 5,260
Navy	8,942	9,057	8,477
Air Force	13,732	14,286	13,686
Defense Agencies	10,093	9,425	10,238
Director of Test & Evaluation, Defense	259	265	—
Director of Operational Test & Evaluation...........	47	31	202

RECAP OF BUDGET ACTIVITIES

	1999	2000^E	2001^E
Basic Research	$ 1,064	$ 1,161	$ 1,217
Applied Research	3,057	3,410	3,144
Advanced Technology Development	3,453	3,826	3,182
Demonstration and Validation..........................	7,364	6,524	6,810
Engineering & Manufacturing Development	7,646	8,679	8,661
RDT&E Management Support	3,553	2,552	2,434
Operational Systems Development....................	11,967	12,137	12,415

RECAP OF FYDP PROGRAMS

	1999	2000^E	2001^E
Strategic Forces	$ 136	$ 179	$ 162
General Purpose Forces	2,776	3,206	2,977
Intelligence and Communications	8,015	7,782	8,134
Mobility Forces	169	284	351
Guard and Reserve Forces	—	—	6
Research and Development (FYDP Program 6)......	26,375	26,194	25,653
Central Supply and Maintenance	315	369	284
Administration and Associated Activities	91	35	49
Support of Other Nations	14	4	7
Special Operations Forces	215	238	241

Source: Department of Defense Budget, "RDT&E Programs (R-1)" (Annually).
NOTE: Detail may not add to totals because of rounding.
  E Estimate. Latest year reflects Administration's budget proposal.

DEPARTMENT OF DEFENSE
PRIME CONTRACT AWARDS
FOR RESEARCH, DEVELOPMENT, TEST, AND EVALUATION
Fiscal Years 1995–1999
(Millions of Dollars)

Program Categories	1995	1996	1997	1998	1999
TOTAL—RDT&E	$21,549	$20,277	$19,856	$20,103	$19,437
Research	1,621	1,603	1,704	1,646	1,785
Exploratory Development	2,331	2,297	1,983	2,053	2,255
Other Development / Support	17,597	16,376	16,168	16,404	15,397
Aircraft—TOTAL	$ 5,770	$ 5,419	$ 4,310	$ 4,609	$ 4,108
Research	10	129	111	207	156
Exploratory Development	119	112	127	106	110
Other Development / Support	5,641	5,178	4,072	4,297	3,842
Missile and Space Systems—TOTAL ...	5,319	5,023	4,904	5,268	4,793
Research	184	210	270	252	188
Exploratory Development	471	493	426	416	536
Other Development / Support	4,663	4,320	4,208	4,600	4,069
Electronics & Communications Equipment—TOTAL	3,495	2,875	3,589	2,955	3,173
Research	196	221	260	170	212
Exploratory Development	350	351	319	312	320
Other Development / Support	2,949	2,303	3,011	2,472	2,640
All Other—TOTAL[a]	6,965	6,960	7,053	7,271	7,364
Research	1,231	1,044	1,064	1,017	1,230
Exploratory Development	1,390	1,341	1,111	1,219	1,289
Other Development / Support	4,344	4,575	4,878	5,035	4,846

Source: Department of Defense, "Prime Contract Awards by Service Category and Federal Supply Classification" (Annually).
NOTE: Detail may not add to totals because of rounding.
a "All Other" includes ships, tank-automotive, weapons, ammunition, services, and other.

DEPARTMENT OF DEFENSE
NET VALUE OF PRIME CONTRACT AWARDS OVER $25,000
FOR RESEARCH, DEVELOPMENT, TEST, AND EVALUATION
By Region and Type of Contractor
Fiscal Year 1999

REGION	TOTAL	Type of Contractor		
		Educational Institutions	Other Non-Profit Institutions[a]	Business Firms
TOTAL—Millions of Dollars	$19,129	$721	$1,597	$16,811
New England	$ 1,637	$371	$ 251	$ 1,015
Middle Atlantic	1,417	72	170	1,175
East North Central	710	40	46	623
West North Central	771	14	4	754
South Atlantic	6,123	76	675	5,372
East South Central	1,425	19	3	1,402
West South Central	683	27	36	620
Mountain	1,926	40	6	1,880
Pacific[b]	4,437	61	406	3,971
PERCENT OF TOTAL	100.0%	100.0%	100.0%	100.0%
New England	8.6%	51.5%	15.7%	6.0%
Middle Atlantic	7.4	10.0	10.6	7.0
East North Central	3.7	5.6	2.9	3.7
West North Central	4.0	1.9	0.2	4.5
South Atlantic	32.0	10.6	42.3	32.0
East South Central	7.4	2.6	0.2	8.3
West South Central	3.6	3.8	2.3	3.7
Mountain	10.1	5.6	0.4	11.2
Pacific[b]	23.2	8.4	25.4	23.6

Source: Department of Defense, "Prime Contract Awards by Region and State" (Annually).
NOTE: Detail may not add to totals because of rounding.
a Includes contracts with other government agencies.
b Includes Alaska and Hawaii.

MISSILE PROGRAMS
RESEARCH, DEVELOPMENT, TEST, AND EVALUATION
By Agency and Model
Fiscal Years 1999, 2000, and 2001
(Millions of Dollars[a])

Agency and Model	1999	2000 [E]	2001 [E]
AIR FORCE			
AMRAAM[b]	$ 38.0	$ 65.6	$ 65.8
*JASSM[b]	122.9	166.4	122.3
JDAM[b]	22.7	18.0	27.4
SFW	7.8	11.6	—
WCMD	11.3	3.9	—
NAVY			
AIM-9X Sidewinder[b]	$ 106.4	$ 117.2	$ 43.4
JSOW[b]	62.1	40.6	22.3
RAM	5.0	6.4	3.8
SRAW	14.7	10.7	0.5
Standard	10.9	1.1	1.2
Tomahawk	149.8	141.4	91.4
Trident II	37.4	36.2	32.1
ARMY			
AAWS-M[b]	$ 4.2	$ 0.7	$ 0.7
ATACMS	39.0	43.0	27.6
BAT	131.9	142.8	96.1
MLRS	25.1	66.6	59.5
SADARM	30.3	24.1	52.8
BMD ORGANIZATION			
BMD	$ 3,283.8	$ 4,267.7	$ 3,943.2

Source: Department of Defense Budget, "Program Acquisition Costs by Weapon System" (Annually).
NOTE: See Missile Programs Chapter for missile program procurement authorization data.
  a Total Obligational Authority.
  b Navy and Air Force funding.
  E Estimate. Latest year reflects Administation's budget proposal.
  NA Not available.
  * Programs in R&D only.

Missile Program Acronyms:

AAWS-M	—Advanced Anti-Tank Weapon System-Medium	AMRAAM	—Advanced Medium Range Air-to-Air Missile
ATACMS	—Army TACtical Missile System	BAT	—Brilliant Anti-Tank submunition
BMD	—Ballistic Missile Defense	JASSM	—Joint Air-to-Surface Standoff Missile
JDAM	—Joint Direct Attack Munition	JSOW	—Joint Standoff Weapon
MLRS	—Multiple Launch Rocket System	RAM	—Rolling Airframe Missile
SADARM	—Sense And Destroy ARmor	SFW	—Sensor Fused Weapon
SRAW	—Short Range Antitank Weapon	WCMD	—Wind Corrected Munitions Dispenser

MILITARY AIRCRAFT PROGRAMS
RESEARCH, DEVELOPMENT, TEST, AND EVALUATION
By Agency and Model
Fiscal Years 1999, 2000, and 2001
(Millions of Dollars[a])

Agency and Model	1999	2000 [E]	2001 [E]
AIR FORCE			
B-2 Spirit	$ 108.6	$ 297.9	$ 48.3
C-17 Globemaster III	120.4	159.0	176.4
C-130J Hercules	—	40.1	60.5
E-8C JSTARS	91.7	147.6	144.1
F-15E Eagle	101.0	126.2	61.3
F-16 Falcon	120.4	114.2	124.9
F-22 Raptor	1,561.8	1,945.1	1,411.8
JPATS[b]	39.0	33.6	22.0
*YAL-1A	252.4	304.2	148.6
NAVY			
AV-8B Harrier	$ 40.1	$ 38.4	$ 38.1
CH-60S	36.8	44.6	13.2
E-2C Hawkeye	45.2	36.3	18.7
EA-6B Prowler	61.0	135.1	55.5
F/A-18E/F Hornet	197.7	141.8	19.2
*JSF[b]	924.9	489.0	856.7
SH-60R	199.7	118.0	69.9
V-22 Osprey	336.1	181.9	148.2
ARMY			
AH-64 Apache	$ —	$ 37.1	$ 17.4
*RAH-66 Comanche	352.2	463.1	614.0
UH-60 Black Hawk	—	9.8	29.9
DEFENSE AIRBORNE RECONNAISSANCE OFFICE			
UAVs	$ 284.0	$ 196.3	$ 251.7

Source: Department of Defense Budget, "Program Acquisition Costs by Weapon System" (Annually).
NOTE: See Aircraft Production Chapter for aircraft program procurement authorization data.
   a Total Obligational Authority.
   b Air Force and Navy funding.
   E Estimate. Latest year reflects Administration's budget proposal.
 NA Not Available.
   * Programs in R&D only.

WHILE THE U.S. MERCHANDISE TRADE DEFICIT BALLOONED $99 billion to a record $329 billion in 1999, the nation's aerospace industry generated a trade surplus of $37 billion—down 8.7% from 1998's record $41 billion.

Aerospace exports—down from $64 billion in 1998 but still strong at $62 billion in 1999—accounted for 9% of all U.S. merchandise exports in 1999. On the other hand, aerospace imports, at $25 billion, increased 8.5% from $23 billion.

Civil exports accounted for 81% of total aerospace exports. The civil export total of $51 billion compares with $52 billion the previous year, a 2.6% decrease.

Exports of civil transport aircraft, which made up half of the civil export volume in 1999, fell 12% to $26 billion. The total for complete civil aircraft, which also includes general aviation aircraft and helicopters, as well as transports, was $28 billion—down from the prior year's $31 billion.

Aircraft engines accounted for another $3.7 billion of the total civil export volume (up from $3.2 billion), while aircraft and engine parts, including spares, totaled $18 billion (up from $17 billion).

Military exports for 1999 declined 2% to $12 billion. Complete military aircraft exports rose 10% to $4.2 billion over the previous year. Exports of aircraft and engine parts decreased 13% to $5.6 billion, while guided missiles, rockets, and parts exports rose 18% to $1.1 billion and

aircraft engines rose a dramatic 58% to $581 million.

The principal customers for U.S. aerospace exports in 1999 were: the United Kingdom ($7.8 billion), Japan ($5.4 billion), France ($5.3 billion), Germany ($4.3 billion), Canada ($3.4 billion), Saudi Arabia ($3.3 billion), China ($2.5 billion), Taiwan ($2.2 billion), Singapore ($2.1 billion), and South Korea ($1.9 billion).

Aerospace imports reached an all-time high at $25 billion, up $2 billion from 1998. Civil imports, at $19 billion, accounted for 75% of the total. That total breaks down into: complete aircraft, $8.8 billion (up from $6.9 billion); aircraft and engine parts, $7.7 billion (down from $7.9 billion); and aircraft engines, $2.3 billion (up from $2 billion).

Military imports amounted to $6.4 billion, up from $6.3 billion. Aircraft and engine parts made up the largest category of military imports at $4.1 billion (down from $4.2 billion), while aircraft engines accounted for $2.3 billion of the total (up from $2 billion).

The principal suppliers of aerospace imports were: France ($6.3 billion), Canada ($5.1 billion), United Kingdom ($5.0 billion), Germany ($2.7 billion), and Japan ($1.7 billion).

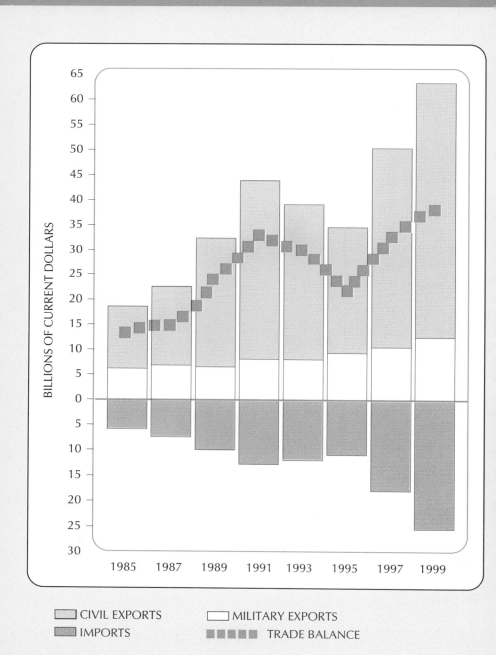

SOURCE: AEROSPACE INDUSTRIES ASSOCIATION

U.S. TOTAL AND AEROSPACE FOREIGN TRADE[a]
Calendar Years 1965–1999
(Millions of Dollars)

Year	Total U.S. Merchandise Trade			Aerospace		
	Trade Balance	Exports	Imports	Trade Balance	Exports	Imports
1965	$ 5,334	$ 26,699	$ 21,366	$ 1,459	$ 1,618	$ 159
1966	3,837	29,379	25,542	1,370	1,673	303
1967	4,122	30,934	26,812	1,961	2,248	287
1968	837	34,063	33,226	2,661	2,994	333
1969	1,289	37,332	36,043	2,831	3,138	307
1970	3,225	43,176	39,952	3,097	3,405	308
1971	(1,476)[b]	44,087	45,563	3,830	4,203	373
1972	(5,729)	49,854	55,583	3,230	3,795	565
1973	2,390	71,865	69,476	4,360	5,142	782
1974	(3,884)	99,437	103,321	6,350	7,095	745
1975	9,551	108,856	99,305	7,045	7,792	747
1976	(7,820)	116,794	124,614	7,267	7,843	576
1977	(28,353)	123,182	151,534	6,850	7,581	731
1978	(30,205)	145,847	176,052	9,058	10,001	943
1979	(23,922)	186,363	210,285	10,123	11,747	1,624
1980	(19,696)	225,566	245,262	11,952	15,506	3,554
1981	(22,267)	238,715	260,982	13,134	17,634	4,500
1982	(27,510)	216,442	243,952	11,035	15,603	4,568
1983	(52,409)	205,639	258,048	12,619	16,065	3,446
1984	(106,703)	223,976	330,678	10,082	15,008	4,926
1985	(117,712)	218,815	336,526	12,593	18,725	6,132
1986	(138,279)	227,159	365,438	11,826	19,728	7,902
1987	(152,119)	254,122	406,241	14,575	22,480	7,905
1988	(118,526)	322,426	440,952	17,860	26,947	9,087
1989	(109,399)	363,812	473,211	22,083	32,111	10,028
1990	(101,718)	393,592	495,311	27,282	39,083	11,801
1991	(66,723)	421,730	488,453	30,785	43,788	13,003
1992	(84,501)	448,164	532,665	31,356	45,018	13,662
1993	(115,568)	465,091	580,659	27,235	39,418	12,183
1994	(150,630)	512,626	663,256	25,010	37,373	12,363
1995	(158,801)	584,742	743,543	21,561	33,071	11,509
1996	(170,214)	625,075	795,289	26,602	40,270	13,668
1997	(180,522)[r]	689,182	869,704[r]	32,239	50,374	18,134
1998[r]	(229,758)	682,138	911,896	40,960	64,071	23,110
1999	(328,821)	695,797	1,024,618	37,381	62,444	25,063

Source: Bureau of the Census, Foreign Trade Division and Aerospace Industries Association, based on data from International Trade Administration.

NOTE: The Commerce Department began reporting international trade using the Harmonized Tariff Schedules of the United States in 1989. Previous years based on the Tariff Schedules of the United States Annotated.

a Total U.S. and aerospace foreign trade are reported as (1) exports of domestic merchandise, including Department of Defense shipments and undocumented exports to Canada, f.a.s. (= free alongside ship) basis, (2) imports for consumption, customs value basis.

b First U.S. trade deficit since 1888.

r Revised.

TOTAL U.S. EXPORTS AND EXPORTS OF AEROSPACE PRODUCTS
Calendar Years 1965–1999
(Millions of Dollars)

Year	TOTAL Exports of U.S. Merchandise[a]	Exports of Aerospace Products				
		TOTAL	Percent of Total U.S. Exports	Civil		Military
				Total	Transports	
1965	$ 26,699	$ 1,618	6.1%	$ 854	$ 353	$ 764
1966	29,379	1,673	5.7	1,035	421	638
1967	30,934	2,248	7.3	1,380	611	868
1968	34,063	2,994	8.8	2,289	1,200	705
1969	37,332	3,138	8.4	2,027	947	1,111
1970	43,176	3,405	7.9	2,516	1,283	889
1971	44,087	4,203	9.5	3,080	1,567	1,123
1972	49,854	3,795	7.6	2,954	1,119	841
1973	71,865	5,142	7.2	3,788	1,664	1,354
1974	99,437	7,095	7.1	5,273	2,655	1,822
1975	108,856	7,792	7.2	5,324	2,397	2,468
1976	116,794	7,843	6.7	5,677	2,468	2,166
1977	123,182	7,581	6.2	5,049	1,936	2,532
1978	145,847	10,001	6.9	6,018	2,558	3,983
1979	186,363	11,747	6.3	9,772	4,998	1,975
1980	225,566	15,506	6.9	13,248	6,727	2,258
1981	238,715	17,634	7.4	13,312	7,180	4,322
1982	216,442	15,603	7.2	9,608	3,834	5,995
1983	205,639	16,065	7.8	10,595	4,683	5,470
1984	223,976	15,008	6.7	9,659	3,195	5,350
1985	218,815	18,725	8.6	12,942	5,518	5,783
1986	227,159	19,728	8.7	14,851	6,276	4,875
1987	254,122	22,480	8.8	15,768	6,377	6,714
1988	322,426	26,947	8.4	20,298	8,766	6,651
1989	363,812	32,111	8.8	25,619	12,313	6,492
1990	393,592	39,083	9.9	31,517	16,691	7,566
1991	421,730	43,788	10.4	35,548	20,881	8,239
1992	448,164	45,018	10.0	36,906	22,379	8,111
1993	465,091	39,418	8.5	31,823	18,146	7,596
1994	512,626	37,373	7.3	30,050	15,931	7,322
1995	584,742	33,071	5.7	25,079	10,606	7,991
1996	625,075	40,270	6.4	29,477	13,624	10,792
1997	689,182	50,374	7.3	40,075	21,028	10,299
1998	682,138[r]	64,071	9.4	51,999	29,168	12,072
1999	695,797	62,444	9.0	50,624	25,694	11,820

Source: Bureau of the Census, Foreign Trade Division and Aerospace Industries Association, based on data from International Trade Administration.
NOTE: International trade reported using Harmonized Tariff Schedules after 1988.
a Includes DoD shipments and undocumented exports to Canada, free alongside ship basis.
r Revised.

U.S. EXPORTS OF AEROSPACE PRODUCTS[a]
BY MAJOR COUNTRIES OF DESTINATION
Calendar Years 1995–1999
(Millions of Dollars)

Major Countries of Destination	1995	1996	1997	1998	1999
Australia	$ 635	$ 939	$ 885	$1,050	$1,426
Brazil	584	715	1,045	1,461	1,575
Canada	2,259	2,704	2,796	3,107	3,438
China	1,250	1,705	2,256	3,731	2,491
Finland	162	1,239	450	602	346
France	1,846	2,013	2,688	4,286	5,322
Germany	1,701	1,907	2,519	4,214	4,325
Israel	604	473	716	1,595	1,789
Italy	1,014	852	629	587	1,426
Japan	3,587	3,772	5,071	6,057	5,401
Korea, South	2,358	2,293	2,479	1,888	1,899
Malaysia	287	330	1,440	1,382	539
Netherlands	2,096	1,368	1,468	1,037	1,566
Saudi Arabia	760	1,707	2,625	5,008	3,299
Singapore	1,544	1,612	2,030	2,296	2,069
Sweden	473	601	443	792	1,295
Switzerland	349	1,707	998	787	608
Taiwan	1,961	1,535	2,407	2,915	2,237
Thailand	395	1,032	1,186	824	618
United Kingdom	2,700	3,400	6,471	7,569	7,845

Source: U.S. Department of Commerce, International Trade Administration.
   a   Includes all civil products, free alongside ship basis; excludes military products whose country of destination are not reported.

U.S. IMPORTS OF AEROSPACE PRODUCTS[a]
BY MAJOR COUNTRIES OF ORIGIN
Calendar Years 1995–1999
(Millions of Dollars)

Major Countries of Origin	1995	1996	1997	1998	1999
Brazil	$ 110	$ 154	$ 371	$ 917	$1,285
Canada	2,461	3,233	3,800	4,867	5,087
France	3,072	3,043	4,087	5,814	6,313
Germany	826	1,039	1,187	2,044	2,707
Israel	354	443	439	493	428
Italy	348	405	480	643	736
Japan	671	1,081	1,728	2,148	1,710
Netherlands	308	142	227	225	161
Singapore	164	204	276	325	87
Sweden	185	342	287	306	147
United Kingdom	2,236	2,634	4,034	5,173	4,968

Source: U.S. Department of Commerce, International Trade Administration.
   a   Includes civil and military products, c.i.f. (Cost, Insurance, and Freight) basis.

117

U.S. EXPORTS OF AEROSPACE PRODUCTS
Calendar Years 1996–1999
(Millions of Dollars)

Aerospace Exports	1996	1997	1998	1999
TOTAL	$40,270	$50,374	$64,071	$62,444
TOTAL CIVIL	$29,477	$40,075	$51,999	$50,624
Complete Aircraft—TOTAL	$15,111	$23,112	$31,427	$28,450
Transports	13,624	21,028	29,168	25,694
General Aviation[a]	598	946	813	1,309
Helicopters	212	207	148	137
Used Aircraft	653	909	1,270	1,286
Other, Incl. Spacecraft[b]	429	520	698	396
Aircraft Engines—TOTAL	1,996	2,092	3,158	3,714
Turbine Engines	1,912	1,995	3,071	3,602
Piston Engines	84	97	87	112
Aircraft and Engine Parts Incl. Spares—TOTAL	11,965	14,373	16,744	18,051
Aircraft Parts & Accessories	8,035	9,196	10,840	11,943
Aircraft Engine Parts	3,930	5,177	5,904	6,108
TOTAL MILITARY	$10,792	$10,299	$12,072	$11,820
Complete Aircraft—TOTAL[c]	$ 3,859	$ 2,397	$ 3,821	$ 4,221
Fighters & Fighter Bombers	3,105	1,823	2,514	2,543
Transports	60	—	618	878
Helicopters	366	391	360	358
Used Aircraft	310	133	213	303
Other, Incl. Spacecraft[b]	315	507	697	509
Aircraft Engines—TOTAL	274	388	367	581
Turbine Engines	213	255	256	500
Piston Engines	62	132	111	81
Aircraft and Engine Parts Incl. Spares—TOTAL	5,164	5,911	6,382	5,557
Aircraft Parts & Accessories	4,543	5,000	5,311	4,558
Aircraft Engine Parts	621	911	1,071	999
Guided Missiles, Rockets, & Parts—TOTAL	1,199	1,146	923	1,091
Guided Missiles & Rockets	504	453	491	576
Missile & Rocket Parts	684	690	431	505
Missile & Rocket Engines	11	3	2	10
Missile & Rocket Engine Parts	—	—	—	—

Source: Aerospace Industries Association, based on data from International Trade Administration.
  a All fixed-wing aircraft under 33,000 pounds.
  b Products within this category are not designated civil or military by the Harmonized Tariff Schedules. Historically, aircraft herein have been predominantly civil. Also, spacecraft not included in "Complete Aircraft—Total."
  c Includes aircraft exported under Military Assistance Programs and Foreign Military Sales.

U.S. IMPORTS OF AEROSPACE PRODUCTS
Calendar Years 1996–1999
(Millions of Dollars)

Aerospace Imports	1996	1997	1998	1999
TOTAL	$13,668	$18,134	$23,110	$25,063
TOTAL CIVIL	$ 9,881	$12,976	$16,837	$18,709
Complete Aircraft—TOTAL	$ 3,924	$ 4,656	$ 6,933	$ 8,773
Transports.................................	823	1,067	2,405	3,397
General Aviation........................	2,136	2,514	3,530	4,279
Helicopters	361	460	536	432
Other, Including Used Aircraft, & Gliders, Balloons, & Airships[a] ...	604	615	461	665
Aircraft Engines—TOTAL	1,019	1,491	2,039	2,257
Turbine Engines[b]........................	969	1,471	2,006	2,233
Piston Engines	50	20	33	23
Aircraft & Engine Parts—TOTAL ...	4,939	6,829	7,866	7,680
Aircraft Parts and Accessories[b]	2,945	4,183	4,901	4,848
Turbine Engine Parts[b]..................	1,777	2,298	2,688	2,327
Piston Engine Parts	85	114	130	110
Spacecraft, Other Parts & Accessories[c]	133	234	147	396
TOTAL MILITARY	$ 3,787	$ 5,159	$ 6,273	$ 6,354
Complete Aircraft—TOTAL	$ 24	$ 13	$ 6	$ 7
Aircraft Engines—TOTAL	1,001	1,510	2,037	2,257
Turbine Engines[b]........................	969	1,471	2,006	2,233
Piston Engines Including Parts	33	38	31	24
Aircraft & Engine Parts—TOTAL ...	2,762	3,636	4,230	4,091
Aircraft Parts[b]	748	1,000	1,252	1,311
Turbine Engine Parts[b].................	1,771	2,296	2,737	2,361
Spacecraft, Missiles, Rockets, Other Parts, & Accessories[bc]	242	340	240	418

Source: Aerospace Industries Association, based on data from International Trade Administration.
NOTE: International trade reported using Harmonized Tariff Schedules after 1989.
  a   Products within this category are not designated civil or military by the Harmonized Tariff Schedules. Historically, these products have been predominantly civil.
  b   Category contains products whose use (civil or military) is unspecified by the Harmonized Tariff Schedules. Figures for those products distributed equally between civil and military.
  c   Includes satellites, propulsion engines, and parts.

119

U.S. EXPORTS OF MILITARY AIRCRAFT[a]
Calendar Years 1995-1999

	1995	1996	1997	1998	1999
TOTAL NUMBER OF AIRCRAFT......	516	429	396	364	309
Fighters and Fighter Bombers	16	78	45	65	68
Transports	7	3	—	12	17
Helicopters	47	41	71	29	75
New Aircraft, NEC........................	387	194	221	163	66
Used or Rebuilt Aircraft	59	113	59	95	83
TOTAL VALUE (Millions of Dollars)	$1,339	$3,859	$2,397	$3,821	$4,221
Fighters and Fighter Bombers	$ 228	$3,105	$1,823	$2,514	$2,543
Transports	453	60	—	618	878
Helicopters	563	366	391	360	358
New Aircraft, NEC........................	33	19	49	119	140
Used or Rebuilt Aircraft	63	310	133	213	303

Source: Aerospace Industries Association, based on data from the International Trade Administration.
a Includes aircraft exported under Military Assistance Programs and Foreign Military Sales.
NEC Not elsewhere classified.

U.S. EXPORTS OF CIVIL AIRCRAFT
Calendar Years 1995–1999

Civil Aircraft Exports	1995	1996	1997	1998	1999
TOTAL NUMBER OF AIRCRAFT[a] ...	1,323	1,309	1,431	1,518	1,451
Helicopters—TOTAL.....................	210	214	259	238	181
Under 2,200 lbs	159	158	199	196	147
Over 2,200 lbs	51	56	60	42	34
General Aviation—TOTAL	363	383	409	399	503
Single-Engine	132	146	188	208	253
Multi-Engine, Under 4,400 lbs	95	88	35	64	66
Multi-Engine, 4,400-10,000 lbs ...	76	94	102	48	113
Multi-Engine, 10,000-33,000 lbs ...	60	55	84	79	71
Transports—TOTAL	137	172	252	375	341
Passenger Aircraft, Over					
33,000 lbs.............................	128	157	239	362	326
Cargo Aircraft, Over 33,000 lbs ...	7	10	10	13	13
Other, Over 33,000 lbs, Incl.					
Pass./Cargo Combi	2	5	3	—	2
Other Aircraft—TOTAL[a]	613	540	511	506	426
Used or Rebuilt Aircraft..............	613	540	511	506	426
Other Aircraft, Including					
Balloons, Gliders, & Kites	398	508	452	526	563
TOTAL VALUE (Millions of Dollars)	$12,275	$15,111	$23,112	$31,427	$28,450
Helicopters—TOTAL.....................	$ 170	$ 212	$ 207	$ 148	$ 137
Under 2,200 lbs	34	27	32	47	24
Over 2,200 lbs	137	185	175	101	113
General Aviation—TOTAL	593	598	946	813	1,309
Single-Engine	74	66	90	100	140
Multi-Engine, Under 4,400 lbs	22	18	14	21	24
Multi-Engine, 4,400-10,000 lbs ...	176	245	349	206	519
Multi-Engine, 10,000-33,000 lbs ...	321	269	493	486	627
Transports—TOTAL	10,606	13,624	21,028	29,168	25,694
Passenger Aircraft, Over					
33,000 lbs.............................	9,354	11,949	19,266	27,700	23,733
Cargo Aircraft, Over 33,000 lbs ...	930	897	1,251	1,468	1,621
Other, Over 33,000 lbs, Incl.					
Pass./Cargo Combi	321	778	512	—	340
Other Aircraft—TOTAL	906	678	932	1,298	1,311
Used or Rebuilt Aircraft..............	876	653	909	1,270	1,286
Other Aircraft, Including					
Balloons, Gliders, & Kites	29	25	22	28	25

Source: Aerospace Industries Association, based on data from International Trade Administration.
NOTE: International trade reported using Harmonized Tariff Schedules after 1988.
   a Numbers of gliders, balloons, & kites excluded from civil aircraft totals.

U.S. IMPORTS OF COMPLETE AIRCRAFT
Calendar Years 1996–1999

Aircraft Imports	1996	1997	1998	1999
TOTAL NUMBER OF AIRCRAFT.........	1,646	1,711	2,024	1,928
Civil Aircraft—TOTAL	1,623	1,685	1,997	1,893
New Complete Aircraft:				
Helicopters	183	240	274	217
General Aviation:				
Single-Engine	100	99	102	162
Multi-Engine, Under 4,400 lbs	—	2	4	3
Multi-Engine, 4,400-10,000 lbs	1	2	3	1
Multi-Engine, Turbojet/Turbofan,				
10,000-33,000 lbs	96	114	171	239
Multi-Engine, Other, Including				
Turboshaft, 10,000-33,000 lbs ...	90	65	60	27
Transports, Multi-Engine, Over				
33,000 lbs..............................	19	27	67	98
Other Civil Aircraft:				
Gliders[a]	144	145	169	92
Balloons & Airships[a]	200	181	170	101
Others including Kites[a]	410	513	666	683
Used or Rebuilt	380	297	311	270
Military Aircraft—TOTAL	23	26	27	35
New Complete Aircraft	14	4	7	9
Used or Rebuilt	9	22	20	26

(Continued on next page)

U.S. IMPORTS OF COMPLETE AIRCRAFT
(Calendar Years 1996–1999, continued)

Aircraft Imports	1996	1997	1998	1999
VALUE (Millions of Dollars).........	$3,947.7	$4,669.0	$6,939.0	$8,779.6
Civil Aircraft—TOTAL	$3,923.5	$4,655.7	$6,932.7	$8,772.7
New Complete Aircraft:				
Helicopters	360.9	460.1	535.7	431.7
General Aviation:				
Single-Engine	57.8	71.8	81.3	145.5
Multi-Engine, under 4,400 lbs	—	0.2	3.6	0.2
Multi-Engine, 4,400-10,000 lbs	8.0	5.4	6.4	4.5
Multi-Engine, Turbojet/Turbofan, 10,000-33,000 lbs	1,286.6	1,795.2	2,860.8	3,879.1
Multi-Engine, Other, including Turboshaft, 10,000-33,000 lbs	783.9	641.1	578.3	249.7
Transports, Multi-Engine, over 33,000 lbs	822.5	1,066.7	2,405.4	3,396.8
Other Civil Aircraft:				
Gliders[a]	1.7	1.8	2.3	1.6
Balloons & Airships[a]	13.0	7.5	12.2	7.2
Others including Kites[a]	1.4	2.2	3.6	7.0
Used or Rebuilt	587.8	603.7	443.1	649.4
Military Aircraft—TOTAL	$ 24.2	$ 13.3	$ 6.3	$ 6.9
New Complete Aircraft	4.7	2.3	1.0	2.5
Used or Rebuilt	19.5	11.0	5.3	4.4

Source: Aerospace Industries Association, based on data from International Trade Administration.
   a   Products within this category are not designated civil or military by the Harmonized Tariff Schedules. Historically, these products have been predominantly civil.

U.S. EXPORTS OF COMMERCIAL TRANSPORT AIRCRAFT[a]
Calendar Years 1995–1999

Region of Destination	1995	1996	1997	1998	1999
TOTAL NUMBER EXPORTED ...	137	172	252	375	341
Canada & Greenland	3	3	—	—	4
Latin America & Caribbean	5	7	11	23	19
Europe	52	52	91	150	169
Middle East	1	5	18	36	55
Asia	71	97	123	150	81
Oceania	2	6	5	9	9
Africa	3	2	4	7	4
TOTAL VALUE (Millions of Dollars)	$10,606	$13,624	$21,028	$29,168	$25,694
Canada & Greenland	$ 280	$ 225	$ —	$ —	$ 237
Latin America & Caribbean	390	566	505	1,215	807
Europe	3,502	3,628	7,538	9,885	11,852
Middle East	157	543	2,449	3,871	3,797
Asia	6,049	8,110	9,916	12,894	7,872
Oceania	126	398	473	628	725
Africa	102	155	147	674	404

Source: Aerospace Industries Association, based on data from the International Trade Administration.
a Airframe weight exceeding 33,000 pounds.

U.S. EXPORTS OF CIVIL HELICOPTERS[a]
Calendar Years 1995-1999

Region of Destination	1995	1996	1997	1998	1999
TOTAL NUMBER EXPORTED	210	214	259	238	181
Canada & Greenland	9	7	9	6	9
Latin America & Caribbean	36	26	36	57	25
Europe	55	64	100	133	100
Middle East	4	2	2	—	1
Asia	50	78	61	26	25
Oceania	25	25	48	14	17
Africa	31	12	3	2	4
TOTAL VALUE (Millions of Dollars)	$170.4	$212.1	$207.1	$148.1	$136.6
Canada & Greenland	$ 7.9	$ 4.3	$ 4.4	$ 8.4	$ 4.8
Latin America & Caribbean	21.1	6.6	21.9	25.6	15.2
Europe	24.3	24.3	56.5	65.8	56.4
Middle East	9.3	0.0	1.1	—	1.6
Asia	83.6	164.7	116.3	43.4	55.1
Oceania	19.0	9.4	4.6	4.7	1.4
Africa	5.3	2.9	2.4	0.3	2.0

Source: Aerospace Industries Association, based on data from the International Trade Administration.
a Excludes used helicopters.

U.S. IMPORTS OF CIVIL HELICOPTERS[a]
Calendar Years 1995-1999

Country of Origin	1995	1996	1997	1998	1999
TOTAL NUMBER IMPORTED	206	183	240	274	217
Canada	172	154	204	189	146
France ....'..	11	16	26	56	47
Germany	15	9	9	12	8
Italy	7	4	1	11	13
Others[b]	1	—	—	6	3
TOTAL VALUE (Millions of Dollars)	$300.2	$360.9	$460.1	$535.7	$431.7
Canada	$262.9	$321.8	$415.3	$419.1	$330.0
France	10.3	20.1	23.7	60.4	50.0
Germany	14.9	8.8	18.3	27.8	20.3
Italy	12.1	10.1	2.9	27.4	31.4
Others[b]	0.0	—	—	1.0	0.1

Source: Aerospace Industries Association, based on data from the International Trade Administration.
a Excludes used helicopters.
b Includes 1 from Israel in 1995; 2 from Australia, 2 from Japan, 1 from Papua New Guinea, and 1 from Poland in 1998; and 2 from Japan and 1 from New Zealand in 1999.

U.S. EXPORTS OF GENERAL AVIATION AIRCRAFT[a]
Calendar Years 1995–1999

Region of Destination	1995	1996	1997	1998	1999
TOTAL NUMBER EXPORTED	363	383	409	399	503
Canada & Greenland	32	32	31	25	22
Latin America & Caribbean	70	67	117	117	181
Europe	135	123	131	140	189
Middle East	10	14	1	10	19
Asia	38	49	44	35	26
Oceania	39	40	45	36	32
Africa	39	58	40	36	34
TOTAL VALUE (Millions of Dollars)	$593.4	$597.5	$945.9	$813.0	$1,309.0
Canada & Greenland	$ 75.8	$ 73.7	$116.0	$101.4	$ 54.6
Latin America & Caribbean	123.0	98.6	282.0	192.8	324.4
Europe	122.6	160.8	220.9	256.0	571.3
Middle East	31.2	17.0	10.8	11.9	96.6
Asia	140.7	92.1	156.5	137.8	97.8
Oceania	47.0	85.5	74.4	52.3	55.7
Africa	53.1	69.7	85.3	60.8	108.5

Source: Aerospace Industries Association, based on data from the International Trade Administration.
a All fixed-wing aircraft under 33,000 pounds.

U.S. IMPORTS OF GENERAL AVIATION AIRCRAFT[a]
Calendar Years 1995–1999

Country of Origin	1995	1996	1997	1998	1999
TOTAL NUMBER IMPORTED ...	259	287	282	340	432
Brazil	11	24	21	58	84
Canada	32	66	87	104	139
France	40	29	50	57	78
Germany	52	34	38	27	26
Israel	3	8	5	9	19
Poland	23	14	10	13	9
Russia	18	10	4	4	3
Sweden	2	25	19	20	1
Switzerland	16	22	25	30	50
United Kingdom	44	43	14	1	—
Other	18	12	9	17	23
TOTAL VALUE (Millions of Dollars)	$1,448.8	$2,136.2	$2,513.7	$3,530.4	$4,279.1
Brazil	$ 74.7	$ 124.0	$ 256.5	$ 782.6	$1,162.8
Canada	494.6	957.8	1,155.2	1,521.9	1,737.5
France	278.8	377.3	748.6	857.3	1,015.8
Germany	242.5	88.3	26.1	39.6	97.6
Israel	21.4	66.1	40.0	81.8	135.1
Poland	2.2	1.6	1.3	1.9	1.3
Russia	1.0	0.8	0.2	0.4	0.4
Sweden	23.0	212.7	153.5	176.6	9.0
Switzerland	32.4	46.6	57.0	66.8	112.7
United Kingdom	276.5	260.2	74.8	0.1	—
Other	1.6	0.9	0.6	1.3	6.9

Source: Aerospace Industries Association, based on data from the International Trade Administration.
a   All fixed-wing aircraft under 33,000 pounds.

U.S. EXPORTS OF AIRCRAFT ENGINES
Calendar Years 1997–1999
(Values in Millions of Dollars)

	1997		1998		1999	
	Number	Value	Number	Value	Number	Value
TOTAL.............................	22,436	$2,479	17,262	$3,525	19,989	$4,295
Turbine Engines	4,679	$2,250	6,339	$3,327	7,980	$4,103
Civil	3,259	1,995	4,249	3,071	5,270	3,602
Military..........................	1,420	255	2,090	256	2,710	500
Piston Engines	17,757	229	10,923	198	12,009	193
Civil, New, Under 500 HP	630	15	806	20	842	19
Civil, New, Over 500 HP ...	315	14	268	5	239	7
Civil, Used	2,054	68	2,843	62	3,941	85
Military..........................	14,758	132	7,006	111	6,987	81

Source: Aerospace Industries Association, based on data from the International Trade Administration.

U.S. IMPORTS OF AIRCRAFT ENGINES[a]
Calendar Years 1997–1999
(Values in Millions of Dollars)

	1997		1998		1999	
	Number	Value	Number	Value	Number	Value
TOTAL.............................	6,347	$2,987	6,586	$4,058	7,726	$4,497
Turbine Engines	3,019	$2,943	3,211	$4,012	3,565	$4,465
Piston Engines	3,328	45	3,375	46	4,161	32
Military..........................	2,859	25	2,760	13	2,252	9
Civil, New, Small	167	1	178	2	336	2
Civil, New, Large	99	2	114	5	824	3
Civil, Used	203	17	323	26	749	18

Source: Aerospace Industries Association, based on data from the International Trade Administration.
a New and used.

EXPORT-IMPORT BANK LENDING AUTHORITY
AND GROSS AUTHORIZATIONS SUMMARY
Fiscal Years 1986–1999
(Millions of Dollars)

LOANS

		Authorizations Summary		
			Direct Loans[a]	
Year	Lending Authority	TOTAL	Direct Credits	Other[b]
1986	$ 1,059	$ 578	$ 371	$ 207
1987	680	599	332	267
1988	693	685	465	220
1989	719	695	517	202
1990	614	614	318	296
1991	750	777	425	352
1992	(c)	817	661	156
1993	(c)	1,748	1,635	113
1994	(c)	3,016	2,980	37
1995	(c)	1,598	1,271	327
1996	(c)	1,236	1,220	16
1997	(c)	1,549	1,465	84
1998	(c)	103	69	34
1999	(c)	903	848	55

GUARANTEES AND INSURANCE

Year	Lending Authority	Authorizations Summary		
		TOTAL	Guarantees	Insurance
1986	$11,484[d]	$ 5,508	$1,128	$4,380
1987	11,355	7,958	1,514	6,444
1988	13,406	5,735	601	5,134
1989	17,901	5,637	1,292	4,345
1990	10,191	8,174	3,333	4,841
1991	11,349	10,588	6,034	4,554
1992	(c)	11,521	7,301	4,220
1993	(c)	13,324	9,095	4,229
1994	(c)	11,870	7,609	4,261
1995	(c)	10,267	5,712	4,555
1996	(c)	10,280	6,412	3,868
1997	(c)	10,610	7,761	2,849
1998	(c)	10,447	6,151	4,296
1999	(c)	12,165	8,299	3,866

Source: Export-Import Bank of the United States.
a The value of Direct Loans may exceed Lending Authority because of the inclusion in Direct Loans of the full amount of Certificates of Loan, portions of which are subsequently sold to commercial banks.
b Includes discount loans, medium term, and small business credits.
c No lending limit set on the value of loans or guarantees and insurance transactions beginning with 1992. Instead the subsidy cost of these transactions limited to $603 million in 1992 and $757 million in 1993. However, in 1993, the combined value of loans, guarantees, and insurance transactions could not exceed $15.5 billion.
d Includes $1,800 million proposed I-MATCH Program which would replace direct lending and would allow an estimated $100 million in commercial loan interest buy-down.

EXPORT-IMPORT BANK
TOTAL AUTHORIZATIONS OF LOANS AND GUARANTEES
AND AUTHORIZATIONS IN SUPPORT OF AIRCRAFT EXPORTS
Fiscal Years 1985–1999
(Millions of Dollars)

Year	TOTAL AUTHORI-ZATIONS	Authorizations in Support of Aircraft Exports			
		TOTAL	Percent of TOTAL Authori-zations	Commercial Jet Aircraft[a]	Other Aircraft[b]
LOANS[c]					
1985	$ 659	$ 39.7	6.0%	$ 12.6	$ 27.1
1986	578	54.6	9.4	46.4	8.2
1987	599	17.0	2.8	13.3	3.7
1988	685	—	—	—	—
1989	695	166.4	23.9	158.0	8.4
1990	614	5.0	0.8	—	5.0
1991	777	—	—	—	—
1992	817	—	—	—	—
1993	1,748	—	—	—	—
1994	3,016	—	—	—	—
1995	1,598	—	—	—	—
1996	1,236	—	—	—	—
1997	1,549	—	—	—	—
1998	103	—	—	—	—
1999	903	590.8	65.4	590.8	—
GUARANTEES					
1985	$1,320	$ 322.4	24.4%	$ 288.9	$ 33.5
1986	1,128	329.2	29.2	277.4	51.8
1987	1,514	808.3	53.4	808.3	—
1988	601	89.2	14.8	73.4	15.8
1989	1,292	496.4	38.4	390.4	106.0
1990	3,333	1,666.3	50.0	224.7	1,441.6
1991	6,034	606.0	10.1	566.9	40.0
1992	7,301	1,667.0	22.8	1,597.1	69.9
1993	9,095	3,488.6	38.4	3,488.6	—
1994	7,609	2,959.0	38.9	2,959.0	—
1995	5,712	977.0	17.1	977.0	—
1996	6,412	1,155.0	18.0	1,155.0	—
1997	7,761	1,959.0	25.2	1,959.0	—
1998	6,151	2,542.5	41.3	2,542.5	—
1999	8,299	5,543.8	66.8	5,543.8	—

Source: Export-Import Bank of the United States.
  a Includes complete aircraft, engines, parts, and retrofits.
  b Includes business aircraft, general aviation aircraft, helicopters, and related goods and services.
  c Loans are commitments for financing by the Eximbank to foreign buyers of U.S. equipment and services, which are made to commercial banks and may subsequently be guaranteed by the Eximbank, in which case the value of the loans is also included with Guarantees.
  d Guarantees by the Export-Import Bank provide assurances of repayment of principal and interest on loans made by private lending institutions, such as commercial banks, for major export transactions. Excludes insurance.

EXPORT-IMPORT BANK
SUMMARY OF COMMERCIAL JET AIRCRAFT AUTHORIZATIONS FOR LOANS[a] AND GUARANTEES[b]
Fiscal Years 1976–1999
(Values in Millions of Dollars)

Year	No. of Jet Aircraft[c]		Export Value[c]		No. of New Commitments		Gross Authorizations	
	Loans	Guarantees	Loans	Guarantees	Loans	Guarantees	Loans	Guarantees
New Authorizations:								
1976	77	6	$1,017	$ 139	34	11	$ 398	$ 87
Tr.Qtr.	15	5	219	182	6	3	94	59
1977	31	25	330	902	16	14	138	294
1978	29	5	479	253	18	5	189	77
1979	118	7	2,938	317	35	10	1,399	239
1980	136	21	3,975	901	36	24	1,693	1,088
1981	121	18	4,568	637	26	17	2,550	533
1982	11	6	441	113	5	2	199	78
1983	21	9	779	619	3	4	384	601
1984	37	8	1,023	327	7	4	532	294
1985	—	14	19	481	1	5	13	289
1986	3	13	74	451	1	9	46	277
1987	—	27	22	1,449	1	14	13	808
1988	—	2	—	94	—	2	—	73
1989	3	5	253	459	1	2	158	390
1990	—	6	—	264	—	2	—	225
1991	—	12	—	665	—	3	—	567
1992	—	37	—	1,889	—	12	—	1,597
1993	—	70	—	4,122	—	27	—	3,489
1994	—	59	—	3,507	—	19	—	2,959
1995	—	27	—	1,205	—	12	—	974
1996	—	18	—	1,089	—	8	—	923
1997	—	34	—	2,357	—	14	—	1,959
1998	—	65	—	3,059	—	24	—	2,543
1999	17	106	1,170	6,464	2	32	591	5,544

Source: Export-Import Bank of the United States.
a Loans are commitments for direct financing by the Export-Import Bank to foreign buyers of U.S. equipment and services, which are made by the Export-Import Bank to commercial banks and which subsequently may be guaranteed by the Export-Import Bank in which case the value of the loans is included with Guarantees.
b Guarantees by the Export-Import Bank provide assurances of repayment of principal and interest on loans made by private lending institutions, such as commercial banks, for major export transactions.
c For Export-Import Bank commitments including both loan and guarantee authorization, number of aircraft and export value reported under "Loans."
Tr.Qtr. See Glossary.

EXPORT-IMPORT BANK
AUTHORIZATIONS OF LOANS AND GUARANTEES
IN SUPPORT OF EXPORTS OF COMMERCIAL JET AIRCRAFT
Fiscal Year 1999
(Values in Millions of Dollars)

Customer (Country/Airline)	Number and Aircraft Model or Related Product	Export Value	Loans (Direct Credits)				Guar-antees
			Amount	Percent Cover-age[a]	Interest Rate	Repay-ment Terms[b]	Amount
FY 1999							
TOTALS	123 aircraft	$7,634	$591	8.2 %	NA	NA	$5,544
Chile/Linea Aerea Nacional Chile	2 x 767	$ 156	$ —	—%	—%	—	$ 130
China/Air China	4 x 737, 1 x 747, 3 x 777	491	—	—	—	—	412
China/China Northern Airlines	2 x MD-90	84	—	—	—	—	66
China/China Southwest Airlines	3 x 737	107	—	—	—	—	113
China/China Xinjiang Airlines	1 x 757	41	—	—	—	—	35
China/Shanghai Airlines ...	1 x 767	72	—	—	—	—	62
China/Wuhan Airlines	1 x 737	32	—	—	—	—	23
China/Zhongyuan Airlines	2 x 737	67	—	—	—	—	55
Czech Republic/ Czech Airlines	2 x 737	67	—	—	—	—	53
Fiji Islands/Air Pacific	—	5	—	—	—	—	4
India/Jet Airways	6 x 737	247	—	—	—	—	198
Indonesia/Republic of Indonesia	11 x 737	384	140	36.6	7.05	48-Q	138
Ireland/Ryanair	5 x 737	110	—	—	—	—	134
Japan/Special Purpose Entity	3 x 747, 1 x 767	532	—	—	—	—	212
Kenya/Kenya Airways	1 x 737	31	—	—	—	—	26
Korea/Korea Air Lines	3 x 747, 3 x 777	786	450	57.3	7.01	40-Q	346

(Continued on next page)

EXPORT-IMPORT BANK
LOAN AND GUARANTEE AUTHORIZATIONS
(Continued)

Customer (Country/Airline)	Number and Aircraft Model or Related Product	Export Value	Loans (Direct Credits)				Guar-antees
			Amount	Percent Cover-age[a]	Interest Rate	Repay-ment Terms[b]	Amount

FY 1999 (continued)

Customer (Country/Airline)	Number and Aircraft Model	Export Value	Amount	Percent Coverage	Interest Rate	Repayment Terms	Guarantees Amount
Morocco/Royal Air Maroc	2 x 737	$ 70	—	—%	—%	—	$ 56
Namibia/Air Namibia	1 x 747	60	—	—	—	—	100
Saudi Arabia/Ministry of Finance	22 x MD-90, 2 x 747, 11 x 777	2,525	—	—	—	—	1,940
Saudi Arabia/Saudi Oger Limited	2 x 737, 1 x 777	189	—	—	—	—	143
Singapore/Singapore Aircraft Leasing Entity ...	1 x 777	118	—	—	—	—	101
South Africa/South African Airways	2 x 747	218	—	—	—	—	186
Taiwan/China Airlines	2 x 737, 1 x 747	213	—	—	—	—	182
Taiwan/Eva Airways	3 x MD-11	328	—	—	—	—	272
Tunisia/Societe Tunisienne De L'air	6 x 737	191	—	—	—	—	162
Turkey/Pegasus Airlines ...	1 x 737	41	—	—	—	—	30
Turkey/Turk Hava Yollari Tao	9 x 737	374	—	—	—	—	273
Uzbekistan/Uzbekistan Airways	2 x 757	95	—	—	—	—	95

Source: Aerospace Industries Assocation, based on data from the Export-Import Bank of the United States.
NOTE: For definitions of Loans and Guarantees, see Export-Import Bank tables on previous pages.
  a   Amount of loan as percent of export value.
  b   Number of payments and frequency (S=semi-annual).

EMPLOYMENT IN THE AEROSPACE INDUSTRY DECLINED IN 1999 after two years of growth. On an annual average employment basis, the industry's work force fell by 50,000, to a total of 846,000, a decline of 5.6% from the previous year. The aircraft manufacturing sector accounted for slightly more than half of the decline.

The 1999 employment figure represented 4.6% of the total employment in all U.S. manufacturing industries; that compares with 4.8% in 1998 and 6.8% at its peak level in the 1989–1990 period. The aerospace work force also represented 7.6% of total employment by U.S. companies engaged in production of durable goods; comparable figures are 8.0% in 1998 and 11.7% at its peak level in 1990.

The largest decline (30,000) was in the aircraft, engines, and parts industry, with an additional 16,000 from the catch-all "other" segment that includes communications, navigation, flight control, displays, and related equipment. The missiles and space vehicles segment accounted for another 4,000.

The total aerospace payroll for 1999 was $31 billion, down from $33 billion the previous year. Both figures include lump-sum payments made by aerospace companies in lieu of general wage increases or cost-of-living adjustments. Expressed as a percentage of the total payroll of all U.S. manufacturing industries ($780 billion), the aerospace payroll amounted to 4.0%, down from 4.4% in 1998.

Weekly earnings by production workers (again including lump-sum payments) averaged $846, down from $848 in the previous year. On average, production workers in airframe fabrication earned $930 per week (down from $934). For other sectors, the average weekly rate was $837 for missiles and space production workers (down from $845), $871 for aircraft engine and engine parts (up from $840), and $735 for aircraft parts and equipment other than engines (down from $751).

Average hourly earnings amounted to $19.82, up from $19.27 in 1998. The average workweek for production workers was 42.7 hours, which compares to 44.0 hours in the previous year.

The number of R&D-performing scientists and engineers in the aerospace industry continued its steep slide in 1999—dropping 14% to 66,400. Aerospace scientists and engineers accounted for only 6.7% of the 997,700 R&D scientists and engineers employed by all U.S. industries known to conduct or finance research and development.

After holding fairly steady at around one million workers through the 1980s and early 1990s, the federal civilian work force in the Department of Defense (DoD) declined—continuing a slide that began in 1993. In 1999, DoD federal civilian employment dropped to 705,826 from 732,097 the previous year, and is projected to continue falling over the next two years.

Employment in NASA programs also declined to 181,469 in 1999 from 183,109 the previous year. NASA directly employed 10% of the total and NASA contractors employed the remaining 90% or 163,000.

ANNUAL AVERAGE EMPLOYMENT IN ALL MANUFACTURING, DURABLE GOODS, AND AEROSPACE INDUSTRIES
Calendar Years 1979–1999
(Thousands of Employees)

Year	All Manu- facturing Industries	Durable Goods Industries	Aerospace Industry[a]		
			TOTAL	As Percent of	
				All Manufac- turing	Durable Goods
1979	21,040	12,730	1,007	4.8%	7.9%
1980	20,285	12,159	1,080	5.3	8.9
1981	20,170	12,082	1,087	5.4	9.0
1982	18,780	11,014	1,038	5.5	9.4
1983	18,432	10,707	1,019	5.5	9.5
1984	19,372	11,476	1,058	5.5	9.2
1985	19,248	11,458	1,151	6.0	10.1
1986	18,947	11,195	1,241	6.6	11.1
1987	18,999	11,154	1,282	6.8	11.5
1988	19,314	11,363	1,294	6.7	11.4
1989	19,391	11,394	1,314	6.8	11.5
1990	19,076	11,109	1,302	6.8	11.7
1991	18,406	10,569	1,214	6.6	11.5
1992	18,104	10,277	1,100	6.1	10.7
1993	18,075	10,221	966	5.3	9.5
1994	18,321	10,448	855	4.7	8.2
1995	18,524	10,683	796	4.3	7.5
1996	18,495	10,789	796	4.3	7.4
1997	18,675	11,010	859	4.6	7.8
1998[r]	18,805	11,205	896	4.8	8.0
1999	18,543	11,103	846	4.6	7.6

Source: Bureau of Labor Statistics, "Employment and Earnings" (Monthly) and Aerospace Industries Association estimates.
a See Glossary for detailed explanation of "Aerospace Employment."
r Revised.

ANNUAL PAYROLL
AEROSPACE INDUSTRY AND ALL MANUFACTURING INDUSTRIES
Calendar Years 1985–1999
(Millions of Dollars)

Year	All Manufacturing Industries[a]	Aerospace Industry[b]			Aerospace As Percent of All Manufacturing
		TOTAL	Production Workers	Other Workers	
1985	$468,500[r]	$26,749	$ 9,837	$16,911	5.7%[r]
1986	480,700[r]	29,547	11,038	18,509	6.1[r]
1987	496,900[r]	31,101	11,700	19,401	6.3
1988	529,900[r]	32,566	11,744	20,822	6.1[r]
1989	547,900[r]	34,154	12,440	21,714	6.2[r]
1990	561,400[r]	35,590	13,020	22,570	6.3[r]
1991	562,500	34,520	12,536	21,984	6.1
1992	583,500	33,123	11,812	21,311	5.7
1993	592,400[r]	30,391	10,673	19,718	5.1
1994	620,300[r]	28,395	9,901	18,494	4.6
1995	647,500[r]	26,603	9,272	17,331	4.1
1996	673,700[r]	27,987	10,105	17,882	4.2[r]
1997	718,800[r]	31,575	12,092	19,483	4.4
1998[r]	757,500	32,981	12,769	20,213	4.4
1999	779,700	31,209	11,703	19,506	4.0

AEROSPACE — INCLUDING LUMP-SUM PAYMENTS[c]

Year	TOTAL	Production Workers	Other Workers	Aerospace As Percent of All Manufacturing
1985	$ 26,782	$ 9,871	$16,911	5.7%[r]
1986	29,611	11,102	18,509	6.2[r]
1987	31,262	11,862	19,401	6.3[r]
1988	32,757	11,935	20,822	6.2[r]
1989	34,396	12,682	21,714	6.3
1990	35,862	13,292	22,570	6.4
1991	34,688	12,704	21,984	6.2
1992	33,257	11,947	21,311	5.7
1993	30,548	10,830	19,718	5.2
1994	28,420	9,926	18,494	4.6
1995	26,618	9,287	17,331	4.1
1996	28,046	10,163	17,882	4.2
1997	31,664	12,181	19,483	4.4
1998[r]	33,000	12,787	20,213	4.4
1999	31,237	11,731	19,506	4.0

Source: Bureau of Economic Analysis, "Survey of Current Business" (Monthly) and Aerospace Industries Association estimates based on Bureau of Labor Statistics, "Employment and Earnings" (Monthly).
a See Glossary for explanation of "Payroll, All Manufacturing."
b Based on combined annual average employment and average weekly earnings for SICs 372 and 376.
c Many aerospace manufacturers have included lump-sum payments in labor settlements since late 1983 in lieu of general wage increases and/or cost of living adjustments. These payments are reported by BLS in separate wage series for SICs 3721 & 3761 and are included by AIA in the totals for production workers and all aerospace.
r Revised.

AEROSPACE FACTS AND FIGURES 2000/2001

EMPLOYMENT IN THE AEROSPACE INDUSTRY[a]
Calendar Years 1985–1999
(Annual Average, Thousands of Employees)

Year	TOTAL	Aircraft, Engines, & Parts (SIC 372)	Missiles & Space Vehicles (SIC 376)	Other[b]
TOTAL EMPLOYMENT				
1985	1,151	616	177	358
1986	1,241	656	200	386
1987	1,282	678	206	399
1988	1,294	684	208	402
1989	1,314	711	194	408
1990	1,302	712	185	405
1991	1,214	669	168	378
1992	1,100	612	146	342
1993	966	542	124	300
1994	855	482	108	266
1995	796	451	98	248
1996	796	458	90	248
1997	859	501	91	267
1998[r]	896	525	92	279
1999	846	495	88	263
PRODUCTION WORKERS				
1985	382	295	62	25
1986	417	323	67	28
1987	434	339	67	29
1988	422	331	63	28
1989	432	344	60	29
1990	430	345	57	29
1991	399	324	48	27
1992	355	291	40	24
1993	308	253	35	20
1994	271	222	31	18
1995	252	208	28	17
1996	260	218	25	17
1997	295	251	25	20
1998[r]	311	267	25	21
1999	285	244	23	19

Source: Bureau of Labor Statistics, "Employment and Earnings" (Monthly) and Aerospace Industries Association estimates.
a See Glossary for detailed explanation of "Aerospace Employment."
b Communications, navigation, flight control, and displays (aerospace-related portions of SICs 366, 381, & 382).
r Revised.

138

EMPLOYMENT IN THE AIRCRAFT, ENGINES, AND PARTS INDUSTRY[a]
Calendar Years 1985–1999
(Annual Average, Thousands of Employees)

Year	TOTAL (SIC 372)	Airframes (SIC 3721)	Engines and Parts (SIC 3724)	Other Parts & Equipment (SIC 3728)
TOTAL EMPLOYMENT				
1985	616.2	325.6	147.5	143.2
1986	655.8	338.9	153.6	163.2
1987	678.0	356.4	158.2	163.4
1988	683.5	368.5	155.8	159.3
1989	711.0	382.2	153.5	175.2
1990	712.3	381.0	151.7	179.5
1991	669.2	355.6	143.2	170.3
1992	611.7	332.1	126.6	153.0
1993	542.0	301.4	109.2	131.4
1994	481.5	271.3	95.1	115.1
1995	450.5	243.6	93.0	113.9
1996	458.1	243.1	94.7	120.4
1997	500.6	262.4	99.8	138.4
1998[r]	525.1	271.6	103.3	150.2
1999	494.9	254.3	100.0	140.7
PRODUCTION WORKERS				
1985	294.6	135.5	74.8	82.2
1986	322.5	146.6	78.7	94.3
1987	338.5	159.1	80.5	96.3
1988	331.3	162.1	77.1	92.1
1989	343.7	167.4	76.8	99.5
1990	344.6	164.1	77.2	103.2
1991	323.6	151.6	73.1	98.8
1992	291.4	137.8	64.3	89.2
1993	252.5	122.7	53.6	76.2
1994	222.0	108.1	46.9	67.0
1995	207.5	93.6	46.2	67.7
1996	217.7	95.6	48.8	73.3
1997	251.1	110.1	53.6	87.4
1998[r]	265.5	114.9	54.0	96.5
1999	243.6	105.2	49.5	88.9

Source: Bureau of Labor Statistics, "Employment and Earnings" (Monthly).
  a   See Glossary for detailed explanation of "Aerospace Employment."
  r   Revised.

AVERAGE HOURLY EARNINGS IN THE AEROSPACE INDUSTRY
Production Workers Only
Calendar Years 1985–1999

Year	TOTAL[a]	Aircraft (SIC 372)				Guided Missiles, Space Vehicles & Parts (SIC 376)	Complete Guided Missiles, & Space Vehicles (SIC 3761)
		TOTAL[a]	Airframes (SIC 3721)	Engines & Parts (SIC 3724)	Other Parts & Equipment (SIC 3728)		
AVERAGE HOURLY EARNINGS[b]							
1985	$12.54	$12.62	$13.18	$12.85	$11.66	$12.14	$12.36
1986	12.75	12.86	13.48	13.08	11.90	12.20	12.48
1987	13.10	13.17	13.74	13.33	12.23	12.73	13.09
1988	13.48	13.55	14.18	13.80	12.28	13.13	13.53
1989	14.10	14.17	14.89	14.42	12.81	13.70	14.20
1990	14.73	14.79	15.66	14.84	13.37	14.39	14.82
1991	15.51	15.60	16.72	15.38	14.05	14.90	15.21
1992	16.46	16.53	17.70	16.28	14.89	15.99	16.45
1993	17.18	17.23	18.43	16.70	15.72	16.80	17.43
1994	17.89	17.95	19.50	17.31	16.01	17.48	18.29
1995	17.99	18.02	19.97	17.34	15.93	17.74	18.58
1996	18.56	18.57	20.49	18.22	16.42	18.51	19.34
1997	18.94	18.88	20.76	18.58	16.76	19.53	20.75
1998	19.24	19.17	21.08	18.93	17.02 [r]	19.96	21.38
1999	19.79	19.75	21.78	19.67	17.38	20.24	21.76
AVERAGE HOURLY EARNINGS INCLUDING LUMP-SUM WAGE PAYMENTS[c]							
1985	$12.69	$12.77	$13.40	$12.85	$11.66	$12.29	$12.56
1986	12.94	13.06	13.80	13.08	11.90	12.33	12.66
1987	13.37	13.48	14.32	13.33	12.23	12.80	13.19
1988	13.73	13.79	14.65	13.80	12.28	13.36	13.87
1989	14.37	14.44	15.41	14.42	12.81	13.98	14.63
1990	15.04	15.10	16.32	14.84	13.37	14.67	15.26
1991	15.71	15.81	17.16	15.38	14.05	15.09	15.49
1992	16.67	16.75	18.18	16.28	14.89	16.05	16.54
1993	17.44	17.52	19.00	16.70	15.72	16.83	17.47
1994	17.96	18.02	19.57	17.31	16.01	17.53	18.37
1995	18.05	18.09	20.02	17.34	15.93	17.77	18.62
1996	18.72	18.74	20.79	18.22	16.42	18.51	19.34
1997	19.09	19.05	21.09	18.58	16.76	19.54	20.76
1998 [r]	19.27	19.19	21.14	18.93	17.02	20.09	21.59
1999	19.82	19.77	21.84	19.67	17.38	20.33	21.90

Source: Bureau of Labor Statistics, "Employment and Earnings" (Monthly) and Aerospace Industries Association estimates.
   a TOTAL columns are employment-based weighted averages.
   b Includes overtime premiums.
   c Many aerospace manufacturers have included lump-sum payments in labor settlements since late 1983 in lieu of general
      wage increases and/or cost of living adjustments. These payments are reported by BLS in separate wage series for SICs 3721
      & 3761 and are included by AIA in totals.
   r Revised.

AVERAGE WEEKLY EARNINGS IN THE AEROSPACE INDUSTRY
Production Workers Only
Calendar Years 1985–1999

| Year | TOTAL[a] | Aircraft (SIC 372) | | | | Guided Missiles, Space Vehicles & Parts (SIC 376) | Complete Guided Missiles, & Space Vehicles (SIC 3761) |
		TOTAL[a]	Airframes (SIC 3721)	Engines & Parts (SIC 3724)	Other Parts & Equipment (SIC 3728)		
AVERAGE WEEKLY EARNINGS[b]							
1985	$531	$534	$547	$542	$506	$515	$527
1986	545	550	568	561	520	517	533
1987	556	558	578	567	523	541	556
1988	573	575	596	582	529	567	585
1989	593	594	616	616	542	589	611
1990	624	626	656	637	570	612	634
1991	648	651	694	654	583	632	649
1992	685	689	736	689	615	652	666
1993	714	717	756	715	657	696	727
1994	754	756	800	753	688	738	779
1995	758	757	809	770	677	765	812
1996	801	802	859	813	721	790	837
1997	844	844	918	838	756	842	896
1998	847	847	932	840	751 [r]	840	892
1999	844	845	928	871	735	836	881
AVERAGE WEEKLY EARNINGS INCLUDING LUMP-SUM PAYMENTS[c]							
1985	$532	$535	$556	$542	$506	$521	$535
1986	548	553	581	561	520	523	541
1987	563	567	603	567	523	544	561
1988	583	584	615	582	529	577	599
1989	605	605	638	616	542	601	629
1990	637	639	684	637	570	624	653
1991	657	659	712	654	583	640	661
1992	693	698	756	689	615	655	670
1993	725	729	779	715	657	697	728
1994	755	758	802	753	688	740	783
1995	759	758	811	770	677	766	814
1996	806	807	871	813	721	790	837
1997	850	851	932	838	756	842	897
1998	848	848	934	840	751 [r]	845	900
1999	846	847	930	871	735	837	887

Source: Bureau of Labor Statistics, "Employment and Earnings" (Monthly) and Aerospace Industries Association estimates.
a   TOTAL columns are employment-based weighted averages.
b   Includes overtime premiums.
c   Many aerospace manufacturers have included lump-sum payments in labor settlements since late 1983 in lieu of general wage increases and/or cost of living adjustments. These payments are reported by BLS in separate wage series for SICs 3721 & 3761 and are included by AIA in totals.
r   Revised.

AVERAGE HOURS IN THE AEROSPACE INDUSTRY
Production Workers Only
Calendar Years 1985–1999

Year	TOTAL[a]	Aircraft (SIC 372)				Guided Missiles, Space Vehicles & Parts (SIC 376)	Complete Guided Missiles, & Space Vehicles (SIC 3761)
		TOTAL[a]	Airframes (SIC 3721)	Engines & Parts (SIC 3724)	Other Parts & Equipment (SIC 3728)		
AVERAGE WEEKLY HOURS							
1985	42.3	42.3	41.5	42.2	43.4	42.4	42.6
1986	42.7	42.8	42.1	42.9	43.7	42.4	42.7
1987	42.4	42.4	42.1	42.5	42.8	42.5	42.5
1988	42.5	42.4	42.0	42.2	43.1	43.2	43.2
1989	42.1	41.9	41.4	42.7	42.3	43.0	43.0
1990	42.3	42.3	41.9	42.9	42.6	42.5	42.8
1991	41.8	41.7	41.5	42.5	41.5	42.4	42.7
1992	41.6	41.7	41.6	42.3	41.3	40.8	40.5
1993	41.6	41.6	41.0	42.8	41.8	41.4	41.7
1994	42.1	42.1	41.0	43.5	43.0	42.2	42.6
1995	42.1	42.0	40.5	44.4	42.5	43.1	43.7
1996	43.1	43.2	41.9	44.6	43.9	42.7	43.3
1997	44.6	44.7	44.2	45.1	45.1	43.1	43.2
1998	44.0	44.2	44.2	44.4	44.1	42.1	41.7
1999	42.7	42.8	42.6	44.3	42.3	41.3	40.5
AVERAGE WEEKLY OVERTIME HOURS							
1985	4.6	4.6	3.5	5.4	5.3	4.6	5.0
1986	4.8	4.9	4.2	5.5	5.5	4.4	4.7
1987	4.8	4.9	4.4	5.0	5.4	4.2	4.3
1988	4.6	4.6	4.3	4.6	5.1	4.5	4.6
1989	5.0	5.1	5.0	5.4	5.0	4.4	4.5
1990	4.5	4.6	4.3	5.3	4.5	3.8	4.1
1991	4.0	4.0	4.1	4.5	3.5	3.9	4.5
1992	3.6	3.7	3.6	4.4	3.3	2.8	3.1
1993	3.8	3.9	3.7	4.6	3.7	2.9	3.2
1994	4.5	4.6	4.1	5.3	4.8	3.7	3.8
1995	4.8	4.9	4.2	5.9	5.2	4.2	4.6
1996	5.7	5.9	5.3	6.5	6.3	3.9	4.2
1997	6.9	7.2	7.2	6.8	7.3	4.3	4.3
1998	5.9	6.1	5.9	6.0	6.3	3.8	3.6
1999	4.5	4.6	4.4	5.5	4.3	3.5	3.0

Source: Bureau of Labor Statistics, "Employment and Earnings" (Monthly) and Aerospace Industries Association estimates.
   a TOTAL columns are employment-based weighted averages.

EMPLOYMENT AND COST OF R&D SCIENTISTS AND ENGINEERS
ALL INDUSTRIES AND AEROSPACE INDUSTRY
Calendar Years 1979–1999

Year	Employment[a]			Cost Per R&D Scientist and Engineer[d]	
	All Industries[b] (Thousands)	Aerospace[c] (Thousands)	Aerospace as a Percent of All Industries	All Industries[b]	Aerospace[c]
1979	423.9	86.5	20.4%	$ 87,400	$ 93,300
1980	450.6	85.9	19.1	94,900	101,600
1981	487.8	95.2	19.5	103,900	128,400
1982	509.8	91.1	17.9	111,600	148,800
1983	540.9	103.1	19.1	116,000	143,600
1984	584.1	111.5	19.1	124,000	156,000
1985	622.5	130.2	20.9	130,200	161,700
1986	671.0	144.8	21.6	128,500	149,800
1987	695.8	136.3	19.6	128,800	180,400
1988	708.6	136.4	19.2	132,300	193,300
1989	722.5	134.8	18.7	134,500	207,300
1990	743.6	115.3	15.5	141,300	213,700
1991	773.4	100.2	13.0	148,600	177,000
1992	779.3	92.9	11.9	157,912	180,552
1993	764.7	97.9	12.8	153,336	176,450
1994	768.5	72.8	9.5	157,459	186,898
1995	746.1	63.5	8.5	167,339	213,328
1996	832.8	95.5	11.5	168,362	170,733
1997	885.7	94.6	10.7	171,495	189,972
1998	951.5	77.0	8.1	173,585	201,493
1999	997.7	66.4	6.7	NA	NA

Source: National Science Foundation.
  a Employment as of January. Scientists and engineers working less than full time have been included in terms of their full time equivalent number.
  b All manufacturing industries and those non-manufacturing industries known to conduct or finance research and development.
  c Standard Industrial Classification codes 372 and 376.
  d The arithmetic mean of the numbers of R&D scientists and engineers reported for January in two consecutive years, divided into the total R&D expenditures of each industry during the earlier year.
NA Not available.

EMPLOYMENT IN NATIONAL AERONAUTICS
AND SPACE ADMINISTRATION PROGRAMS
End of Fiscal Years 1962–2001

Year	TOTAL	NASA Employees	Contractor Employees [a]
1962	137,656	22,156	115,500
1963	246,304	27,904	218,400
1964	379,084	31,984	347,100
1965	409,900	33,200	376,700
1966	393,924	33,924	360,000
1967	306,926	33,726	273,200
1968	267,871	32,471	235,400
1969	218,345	31,745	186,600
1970	160,850	31,350	129,500
1971	143,578	29,478	114,100
1972	138,800	27,500	111,300
1973	134,850	26,850	108,000
1974	125,220	25,020	100,200
1975	127,733	24,333	103,400
1976	130,739	24,039	108,000
1977	124,136	23,636	100,500
1978	124,637	23,237	101,400
1979	131,931	22,831	109,100
1980	135,613	22,613	113,000
1981	133,473	21,873	111,600
1982	128,730	22,430	106,300
1983	129,246	22,246	107,000
1984	162,080	22,080	140,000
1985	131,991	21,991	110,000
1986	154,660	21,660	133,000
1987	165,001	22,001	143,000
1988	172,326	22,326	150,000
1989	213,054	23,054	190,000
1990	221,829	23,829	198,000
1991	223,149	24,149	199,000
1992	230,513	24,513	206,000
1993	228,674	24,174	204,500
1994	217,910	23,873	194,037
1995	209,355	22,355	187,000
1996	198,113	21,113	177,000
1997	189,070	20,070	169,000
1998	183,109	19,109	164,000
1999	181,469	18,469	163,000
2000 [E]	177,600	18,600	159,000
2001 [E]	177,000	19,000	158,000

Source: Office of Management and Budget, "Budget of the United States Government" (Annually) and NASA Headquarters.
   a   Includes estimates of manpower for hardware and related contracts, as well as actual work-years for support service contracts. Increase in FY 1984 caused by change in estimating methodology to reflect more accurately the mix of support and development contractors.
   E   Estimate.

FEDERAL CIVILIAN EMPLOYMENT[a]
IN THE DEPARTMENT OF DEFENSE
Fiscal Years 1967–2001

Year	TOTAL	Civil Functions[b]	Military Functions[c]
1967	1,225,637	31,980	1,193,657
1968	1,288,130	32,062	1,256,068
1969	1,257,091	31,214	1,225,877
1970	1,159,935	30,293	1,129,642
1971	1,092,804	30,063	1,062,741
1972	1,040,147	30,585	1,009,562
1973	987,281	29,971	957,310
1974	1,002,850	29,072	973,778
1975	983,790	29,069	954,721
1976	951,034	28,648	922,386
1977	940,549	28,912	911,637
1978	933,071	28,962	904,109
1979	914,582	28,592	885,990
1980	907,700	27,700	880,000
1981	981,400	34,400	947,000
1982	1,009,192	31,111	978,081
1983	1,015,622	30,816	984,806
1984	1,040,213	28,681	1,011,532
1985	1,065,624	28,754	1,036,870
1986	1,069,863	28,511	1,041,352
1987	1,059,669	28,352	1,031,317
1988	1,053,000	28,419	1,024,581
1989	1,051,166	28,081	1,023,085
1990	1,048,814	27,651	1,021,163
1991	1,001,183	27,385	973,798
1992	1,000,453	27,584	972,869
1993	958,855	27,055	931,800
1994	896,293	28,001	868,292
1995	849,529	27,790	821,739
1996	806,122	27,180	778,942
1997	771,914	26,164	745,750
1998	732,097[r]	24,855	707,242[r]
1999	705,826	24,800	680,996
2000[E]	686,200	24,700	661,500
2001[E]	670,200	24,700	645,500

Source: Office of Management and Budget, "The Budget of the United States Government" (Annually).
a   Full-time equivalent civilian employment.
b   Data are estimated for portions of Civil Functions.
c   The Department of Defense is exempt from full-time equivalent controls. Data shown are estimated civilian employment for military functions and military assistance.
E   Estimate.
r   Revised.

OCCUPATIONAL INJURY AND ILLNESS INCIDENCE RATES[a]
ALL MANUFACTURING AND AEROSPACE INDUSTRIES
Calendar Years 1994–1998

	1994	1995	1996	1997	1998
All Manufacturing:					
Total Cases	12.2	11.6	10.6	10.3	9.7
Lost Workday Cases	5.5	5.3	4.9	4.8	4.7
Nonfatal Cases without Lost Workdays	6.8	6.3	5.7	5.4	5.0
Aircraft and Parts (SIC 372):					
Total Cases	9.7	8.8	7.9	8.7	8.7
Lost Workday Cases	4.0	3.6	3.4	3.8	4.2
Nonfatal Cases without Lost Workdays	5.7	5.3	4.5	4.9	4.5
Aircraft (SIC 3721):					
Total Cases	9.4	8.7	7.3	8.5	8.9
Lost Workday Cases	3.8	3.4	3.0	3.7	4.3
Nonfatal Cases without Lost Workdays	5.7	5.3	4.3	4.8	4.6
Aircraft Engines and Parts (SIC 3724):					
Total Cases	10.0	8.3	7.9	7.7	6.2
Lost Workday Cases	3.8	3.4	3.6	3.3	2.8
Nonfatal Cases without Lost Workdays	6.2	4.9	4.3	4.5	3.4
Aircraft Parts (SIC 3728):					
Total Cases	10.0	9.5	9.1	9.9	10.0
Lost Workday Cases	4.6	4.1	3.9	4.5	5.0
Nonfatal Cases without Lost Workdays	5.5	5.4	5.2	5.4	5.0
Guided Missiles, Space Vehicles & Parts (SIC 376):					
Total Cases	4.5	4.0	3.4	3.2	3.3
Lost Workday Cases	1.8	1.8	1.3	1.5	1.5
Nonfatal Cases without Lost Workdays	2.7	2.2	2.0	1.7	1.8
Guided Missiles & Space Vehicles (SIC 3761):					
Total Cases	4.2	3.7	3.0	2.9	3.0
Lost Workday Cases	1.6	1.5	1.2	1.3	1.3
Nonfatal Cases without Lost Workdays	2.6	2.1	1.8	1.6	1.8
Space Propulsion Units & Parts (SIC 3764):					
Total Cases	4.3	NA	NA	NA	3.2
Lost Workday Cases	1.7	NA	NA	NA	1.6
Nonfatal Cases without Lost Workdays	2.5	NA	NA	NA	1.7
Other Space Vehicle Equipment (SIC 3769):					
Total Cases	6.5	5.8	NA	NA	4.3
Lost Workday Cases	2.8	3.0	NA	NA	2.6
Nonfatal Cases without Lost Workdays	3.7	2.8	NA	NA	1.8

Source: Bureau of Labor Statistics, "Survey of Occupational Injuries and Illnesses" (Annually).
   a   Defined as the number of injuries and illnesses per 100 full-time workers. Separate incidence rates also available for occupational injuries only.
   NA   Not available.

AEROSPACE INDUSTRY WORK STOPPAGES[a]
Calendar Years 1979-1999

Year	Number of Strikes[b]	Number of Workers Involved	Work-Days Idle in Year
1979	12	6,600	103,400
1980	17	4,400	92,900
1981	12	6,100	188,900
1982 [c]	4	11,900	45,200
1983	2	8,700	404,100
1984	4	14,600	188,200
1985	4	19,700	289,800
1986	—	—	—
1987	—	—	—
1988	3	10,600	415,800
1989	2	58,500	1,848,000
1990	1	2,300	56,700
1991	1	1,500	—
1992	1	3,800	11,400
1993	2	27,800	34,600
1994	—	—	—
1995	1	33,000	1,551,000
1996	2	7,800	90,100
1997	—	—	—
1998	—	—	—
1999	—	—	—

Source: Bureau of Labor Statistics, "Compensation and Working Conditions" (Monthly).
  a Based on SIC 372 of the 1967 Code, which includes missile and space propulsion units and parts and missile and space
     vehicle equipment not elsewhere classified, but which excludes complete guided missiles and space vehicles.
  b Strikes beginning during calendar year.
  c Effective 1982, data not available for work stoppages involving fewer than 1,000 employees.

IN 1999, THE AEROSPACE INDUSTRY REPORTED NET PROFITS of $10 billion, a substantial gain over 1998, reflecting record sales. Expressed as a percentage of sales, the industry's profit amounted to 6.5%. This was higher than the 6.2% average for all U.S. manufacturing industries. It also marked a rise from 1998's aerospace profit-to-sales ratio of 5.0%. As a percentage of assets, the 1999 aerospace figure was 6.2%, up from 4.8% in the previous year. As a percentage of equity, aerospace earnings were 21.8%, a significant increase from 18.0% in 1998.

The aerospace balance sheet for 1999 showed net working capital of $11.7 billion, up slightly from $11.5 billion in 1998. Stockholders' equity jumped 17% to $50 billion in 1999, while total assets climbed $10 billion to $170 billion.

Lockheed Martin Corporation again topped the list of DoD's prime contractors in FY 1999 with contracts totaling $12.7 billion. In second place was The Boeing Company with $11.6 billion. The Raytheon Company, at $6.4 billion, ranked third. Rounding out the top 10 were: General Dynamics Corporation ($4.6 billion), Northrop Grumman Corporation ($3.2 billion), United Technologies Corporation ($2.4 billion), Litton Industries, Inc. ($2.1 billion), General Electric Company ($1.7 billion), TRW Incorporated ($1.4 billion), and Textron, Inc. ($1.4 billion).

Geographically, for the third year the South Atlantic region topped the list of DoD prime contract awards for aircraft production, ahead of both the Pacific and the West North Central regions. The South Atlantic region received contracts worth $5.8 billion, or 22.7% of the total. The Pacific region was second with $5.2 billion (20.4%), and the West North Central region was third with $4.3 billion (16.7%).

In DoD missile/space contract awards, the Pacific region showed a slight decrease but remained far out in front with $4.2 billion (37.3%). In second place was the Mountain region with $2.7 billion (24.1%), and in third was the South Atlantic region with $1.2 billion (11.1%).

The South Atlantic region also led in DoD awards for electronics and communications equipment with $4.7 billion (36.2%); the Pacific region was second with $2 billion (15.2%); and the Middle Atlantic was third with $1.7 billion (13.4%).

For the first time, United Space Alliance topped the list of NASA contractors, with contracts in FY 1999 worth $1.5 billion. The rest of the top 10 included: The Boeing Company ($1.2 billion), Lockheed Martin Corporation ($906 million), McDonnell Douglas Corporation ($416 million), Thiokol Corporation ($395 million), Lockheed Mar-tin Space Operations Company ($296 million), Boeing North America ($272 million), Lockheed Martin Engineering and Science ($231 million), Space Gateway Support ($221 million), and TRW Inc. ($184 million).

INCOME STATEMENT AND OPERATING RATIOS
FOR AEROSPACE COMPANIES[a]
Calendar Years 1996–1999
(Millions of Dollars)

INCOME STATEMENT	1996	1997	1998	1999
Net Sales, Receipts, Operating Revenues	$127,051	$139,287	$154,606	$157,087
Less: Depreciation, Depletion, & Amortization of Property, Plant, and Equipment	4,134	4,011	4,201	4,212
Less: All Other Operating Costs & Expenses, Including Selling Costs & General & Administrative Expenses	112,792	125,712	139,118	140,228
Income (or Loss) from Operations	$ 10,125	$ 9,564	$ 11,287	$ 12,648
Net Non-Operating Income (Expense)	8	400	(431)	1,775
Income (or Loss) before Income Taxes (= Total Income)	$ 10,132	$ 9,964	$ 10,855	$ 14,423
Less: Provision for Current & Deferred Domestic Income Taxes	2,982	2,743	3,155	4,208
Income (or Loss) after Income Taxes (= Net Profit)	$ 7,150	$ 7,221	$ 7,701	$ 10,214
Cash Dividends Charged to Retained Earnings	2,071	2,707	2,397	2,501
Net Income Retained in Business	$ 5,078	$ 4,512	$ 5,304	$ 7,713
Retained Earnings at Beginning of Year[b]	30,225	29,973	31,130	34,832
Adjustments to Retained Earnings[c]	(1,189)	(3,330)	(42)	(607)
Retained Earnings at End of Year[d]	$ 34,115	$ 31,157	$ 36,392	$ 41,938

OPERATING RATIOS

Income before Taxes as Percent of Net Sales	8.0%	7.2%	7.0%	9.2%
Provision for Current & Deferred Domestic Income Taxes as Percent of Income before Taxes (Total Income)	29.4	27.5	29.1	29.2
Income after Taxes (Net Profit) as Percent of Net Sales	5.6	5.2	5.0	6.5
Income after Taxes (Net Profit) as Percent of Stockholders' Equity[e]	17.1	17.3	18.0	21.8
Income after Taxes (Net Profit) as Percent of Total Assets[e]	5.1	4.8	4.8	6.2

Source: Bureau of the Census, "Quarterly Financial Report for Manufacturing, Mining, and Trade Corporations" (Quarterly).
NOTE: Detail may not add to totals because of rounding.
a Based on sample of corporate entities classified in SIC codes 372 and 376, having as their principal activity the manufacture of aircraft, guided missiles, space vehicles, and their propulsion, and parts.
b Beginning-of-year retained earnings for any particular year do not equal end-of-year retained earnings for the previous year because of rotation of small companies in survey sample.
c Other direct credits (or charges) to retained earnings (net), including stock and other non-cash dividends, etc.
d Retained Earnings at End of Year CALCULATED AS Retained Earnings at Beginning of Year PLUS Income (Loss) after Income Taxes MINUS Cash Dividends Charged to Retained Earnings PLUS Adjustments to Retained Earnings.
e Average of four quarters.

BALANCE SHEET FOR AEROSPACE COMPANIES[a]
December 31, 1996–1999
(Millions of Dollars)

	1996	1997	1998	1999
Assets:				
Current Assets:				
Cash	$ 4,051	$ 3,017	$ 1,918	$ 2,898
Securities, Commercial Paper, & Other Short-term Financial Investments	5,025	4,466	2,364	3,165
Total Cash and U.S. Government and Other Securities	$ 9,076	$ 7,484	$ 4,283	$ 6,063
Receivables (Total)	18,130	18,970	16,765	18,082
Inventories (Gross)	30,873	43,411	46,578	41,216
Other Current Assets	5,531	7,312	7,730	8,320
Total Current Assets	$ 63,611	$ 77,176	$ 75,356	$ 73,681
Net Plant, Property, & Equipment	24,272	24,819	26,721	28,613
Other Non-Current Assets	48,054	48,243	57,779	67,701
Total Assets...	$135,937	$150,238	$159,856	$169,995
Liabilities:				
Current Liabilities:				
Short Term Loans.............................	$ 1,951	$ 1,866	$ 4,178	$ 4,009
Trade Accounts & Notes Payable	10,688	11,330	11,634	11,001
Income Taxes Accrued	2,410	2,160	2,429	1,987
Installments Due on Long Term Debts ...	918	2,567	2,098	1,793
Other Current Liabilities	31,683	45,094	43,524	43,204
Total Current Liabilities.......................	$ 47,650	$ 63,019	$ 63,862	$ 61,994
Long Term Debt	28,091	26,545	28,937	33,485
Other Non-Current Liabilities	20,370	21,349	23,987	24,173
Total Liabilities	$ 96,110	$110,914	$116,787	$119,652
Stockholders' Equity:				
Capital Stock	$ 10,004	$ 9,438	$ 8,027	$ 5,682
Retained Earnings	29,824	29,886	35,043	44,661
Total Stockholders' Equity	$ 39,828	$ 39,324	$ 43,069	$ 50,343
Total Liabilities & Stockholders' Equity	$135,937	$150,238	$159,856	$169,995
Net Working Capital.............................	$ 15,961	$ 14,157	$ 11,494	$ 11,688

Source: Bureau of the Census, "Quarterly Financial Report for Manufacturing, Mining, and Trade Corporations" (Quarterly).
NOTE: Detail may not add to totals because of rounding.
   a   Based on sample of corporate entities classified in SIC codes 372 and 376, having as their principal activity the manufacture of aircraft, guided missiles, space vehicles, their propulsion, and parts.

NET PROFIT AFTER TAXES
AS A PERCENT OF SALES, ASSETS, AND EQUITY
FOR ALL MANUFACTURING CORPORATIONS
AND THE AEROSPACE INDUSTRY
Calendar Years 1985–1999

PERCENT OF SALES

Year	All Manufacturing Corporations	Non-Durable Goods	Durable Goods	Aerospace[a] Industry
1985	3.8%	4.1%	3.4%	3.1%
1986	3.7	4.6	2.9	2.8
1987	4.9	5.2	4.5	4.1
1988	6.0	6.7	5.2	4.3
1989	5.0	5.8	4.1	3.3
1990	4.0	4.9	3.0	3.4
1991	2.5	4.2	0.6	1.8[b]
1992	1.0	3.2	(1.4)	(1.4)[b]
1993	2.8	3.7	1.9	3.6
1994	5.4	5.5	5.2	4.7
1995	5.7	6.1	5.3	3.8
1996	6.0	6.6	5.5	5.6
1997	6.2	6.6	5.8	5.2
1998	6.0	6.1	5.9	5.0
1999	6.2	6.2	6.2	6.5

Year	Percent of Assets[c]		Percent of Equity[c]	
	All Manufacturing	Aerospace[a] Industry	All Manufacturing	Aerospace[a] Industry
1985	4.6%	3.6%	10.1%	11.1%
1986	4.2	3.1	9.5	9.4
1987	5.6	4.4	12.8	14.6
1988	6.9	4.4	16.2	14.9
1989	5.6	3.3	13.7	10.7
1990	4.3	3.4	10.7	11.5
1991	2.6	1.9[b]	6.4	6.1[b]
1992	1.0	(1.2)[b]	2.6	(5.2)[b]
1993	2.9	3.5	8.1	13.2
1994	5.8	4.3	15.6	14.8
1995	6.2	3.5	16.2	11.1
1996	6.5	5.1	16.8	17.1
1997	6.6	4.8	16.6	17.3
1998	6.1	4.8	15.7	18.0
1999	6.1	6.2	16.5	21.8

Source: Bureau of the Census, "Quarterly Financial Report for Manufacturing, Mining, and Trade Corporations" (Quarterly).
 a Based on a sample of corporate entities classified in SIC codes 372 and 376, having as their principal activity the manufacture of aircraft, guided missiles, space vehicles, their propulsion, and parts.
 b Reflects unusually large non-operating expenses totalling $3.4 and $8.7 billion in 1991 and 1992, respectively, due to restructuring changes and the implementation of a change in accounting for future retirement benefit costs.
 c Average of four quarters
 ( ) Net loss after taxes.

NEW CAPITAL EQUIPMENT EXPENDITURES
Calendar Years 1967–1998
(Millions of Dollars)

Year	All Manufacturing Industries	Aerospace Industry[a]	Aircraft, Engines, & Parts	Missiles, Space Vehicles, & Parts
1967	$ 21,503	$ 520	$ 408	$ 111
1968	20,613	399	282	117
1969	22,291	429	340	89
1970	22,164	244	181	62
1971	20,941	115	59	56
1972	24,073	261	169	92
1973	26,979	362	258	104
1974	35,696	407	283	124
1975	37,262	478	369	109
1976	40,545	557	431	126
1977	47,459	673	508	164
1978	55,209	948	775	174
1979	61,533	1,551	1,301	250
1980	70,113	1,923	1,618	306
1981	78,632	2,006	1,637	369
1982	74,562	2,142	1,680	462
1983	61,931	2,159	1,530	629
1984	75,186	3,050	2,091	960
1985	83,058	3,784	2,429	1,356
1986	76,355	4,145	2,818	1,327
1987	78,650	3,612	2,536	1,075
1988	81,593	3,388	2,362	1,026
1989	98,738	3,921	2,800	1,121
1990	105,018	3,490	2,621	869
1991	103,003	3,407	2,823	584
1992	103,188	3,860	3,384	476
1993	103,133	2,725	2,307	418
1994	112,784	2,363	1,969	395
1995	128,473	2,114	1,734	380
1996	139,323	2,513	2,023	490
1997	151,735	3,130	2,378	752
1998	151,905	3,475	2,622	853

Source: Bureau of the Census.
   a Combined total for establishments in Aircraft, Missiles, Space Vehicles, and Parts Manufacturing.

DEPARTMENT OF DEFENSE
PRIME CONTRACT AWARDS OVER $25,000
FOR SELECTED MAJOR MILITARY HARD GOODS
By Geographic Region
Fiscal Years 1997, 1998, and 1999

Program and Region	Millions of Dollars			Percent of Program Total		
	1997	1998	1999	1997	1998	1999
AIRCRAFT—TOTAL	$21,066	$22,690	$25,673	100.0%	100.0%	100.0%
New England	$ 1,749	$ 1,493	$ 1,890	8.3%	6.6%	7.4%
Middle Atlantic	1,272	1,348	1,657	6.0	5.9	6.5
East North Central	1,376	1,441	1,467	6.5	6.4	5.7
West North Central	4,093	4,298	4,276	19.4	18.9	16.7
South Atlantic	5,085	5,455	5,818	24.1	24.0	22.7
East South Central	380	417	526	1.8	1.8	2.0
West South Central	2,529	2,658	3,212	12.0	11.7	12.5
Mountain....................	432	1,084	1,581	2.1	4.8	6.2
Pacific[a]	4,150	4,496	5,248	19.7	19.8	20.4
MISSILE & SPACE SYSTEMS—TOTAL.........	$11,180	$11,152	$11,162	100.0%	100.0%	100.0%
New England	$ 1,066	$ 838	$ 589	9.5%	7.5%	5.3%
Middle Atlantic	802	368	309	7.2	3.3	2.8
East North Central	82	147	175	0.7	1.3	1.6
West North Central	243	306	195	2.2	2.7	1.7
South Atlantic	1,382	1,373	1,237	12.4	12.3	11.1
East South Central	665	626	583	5.9	5.6	5.2
West South Central	989	983	1,219	8.8	8.8	10.9
Mountain....................	1,479	2,014	2,693	13.2	18.1	24.1
Pacific[a]	4,471	4,498	4,163	40.0	40.3	37.3
ELECTRONICS & COMMUNICATIONS EQUIPMENT—TOTAL ...	$14,024	$12,813	$12,949	100.0%	100.0%	100.0%
New England	$ 1,194	$ 1,163	$ 1,593	8.5%	9.1%	12.3%
Middle Atlantic	1,983	1,880	1,736	14.1	14.7	13.4
East North Central	960	841	666	6.8	6.6	5.1
West North Central	401	534	573	2.9	4.2	4.4
South Atlantic	5,083	4,198	4,691	36.2	32.8	36.2
East South Central	162	204	226	1.2	1.6	1.7
West South Central	744	774	872	5.3	6.0	6.7
Mountain....................	631	617	621	4.5	4.8	4.8
Pacific[a]	2,865	2,602	1,971	20.4	20.3	15.2

Source: Department of Defense, "Prime Contract Awards by Region and State" (Annually).
NOTE: Detail may not add to totals because of rounding.
a Includes Alaska and Hawaii.

DEPARTMENT OF DEFENSE MAJOR CONTRACTORS
Fiscal Years 1995–1999
Listed by rank according to net value of
prime contracts awarded during last fiscal year
(Millions of Dollars)

Company	1995	1996	1997	1998	1999
TOTAL CONTRACTS	$117,552	$119,556	$116,680	$118,139	$125,037
Lockheed Martin Corp.[b]	$ 12,450	$ 11,998	$ 11,638	$ 12,341	$ 12,675
The Boeing Co.[c]....................	11,011	12,951	9,645	10,866	11,568
Raytheon Co.[d]	5,883	6,252	5,693	5,661	6,401
General Dynamics Corp.[e].........	2,258	2,670	3,012	3,680	4,564
Northrop Grumman Corp.[f]	2,913	2,605	3,476	2,691	3,193
United Technologies Corp.	1,775	2,258	1,810	1,983	2,368
Litton Industries Inc.	1,237	1,709	1,603	1,644	2,097
General Electric Co.	2,104	1,530	1,677	1,161	1,714
TRW Inc.[g]	1,254	1,194	1,163	1,346	1,431
Textron Inc.	1,069	1,194	1,445	1,838	1,423
Science Applications Int'l Corp.	931	1,065	1,095	1,224	1,358
Carlyle Group[h]	486	877	611	1,329	1,336
AlliedSignal Inc.....................	503	512	547	655	746
Computer Sciences Corp.	656	712	704	647	744
General Electric Co. PLC	124	194	247	732	729
ITT Industries Inc.	648	671	790	781	659
Halliburton Co.	276	574	290	286	658
Humana Inc.	(a)	188	621	868	620
Bechtel Corp.	212	179	267	201	600
Foundation Health Systems Inc.	(a)	(a)	656	593	580
Dyncorp	448	380	535	537	566
Newport News Shipbuilding Inc.	3,710	(a)	720	1,546	535
Adminastar Inc.	(a)	(a)	(a)	217	511
Westinghouse Electric Corp. ...	1,225	1,441	777[i]	567[i]	492[i]
IT Group Inc.	219	145	(a)	436	459
Longbow Limited Liability Co....	(a)	274	338	331	426
Alliant Techsystems Inc.	473	457	378	317	422
Mitre Corp.	370	375	304	394	417
Triwest Healthcare Alliance Co.	(a)	(a)	213	420	414
Sverdrup Corp.	153	232	328	256	406

Source: Department of Defense, "100 Companies Receiving the Largest Dollar Volume of Prime Contract Awards" (Annually).
 a   Not in top 100 companies for indicated year(s).
 b   Includes awards previously reported separately as Martin Marietta Corp., Lockheed Corp., and Loral Corp.
 c   Includes awards previously reported separately as McDonnell Douglas Corp. and Rockwell International Corp.
 d   Includes awards previously reported as E-Systems Inc. and General Motors Corp.
 e   Includes awards previously reported as Bath Holding Corp.
 f   Includes awards previously reported as Grumman Corporation.
 g   Includes awards previously reported separately as BDM International Inc.
 h   Listed previously as United Defense Limited Partnership and FMC Corp.
 i   Listed as CBS Corp.

NATIONAL AERONAUTICS AND SPACE ADMINISTRATION
MAJOR CONTRACTORS
Fiscal Years 1996–1999
By rank according to net value of NASA prime
contracts awarded during last fiscal year
(Millions of Dollars)

Company	1996	1997	1998	1999
TOTAL PROCUREMENTS...............	$12,699	$12,790	$12,561	$12,675
Awards to Business Firms...............	9,801	9,817	9,551	9,386
% of TOTAL PROCUREMENTS	77%	77%	76%	74%
United Space Alliance LLC[b]	$ 870	$1,314	$1,480	$1,465
The Boeing Co.	1,608	1,662	1,488	1,205
Lockheed Martin Corp.[c]	833	1,049	982	906
McDonnell Douglas Corp.	389	354	420	416
Thiokol Corp.	396	424	364	395
Lockheed Martin Space Operations Co.	34	27	36	296
Boeing North America[d]..................	756	237	261	272
Lockheed Martin Engrg. & Science ...	166	376	227	231
Space Gateway Support	(a)	(a)	(a)	221
TRW Inc......................................	287	281	224	184
Hughes Aircraft Co.	153	153	108	174
Computer Sciences Corp.	214	163	177	174
Hughes Information Tech. Corp.......	133	117	92	123
United Technologies Corp.	162	140	91	104
Raytheon STX Corp.[f]	47	43	52	92
Science Applications Int'l Corp.	30	58	78	91
AlliedSignal Technical Services	285	333	275	85
Lockheed Martin Aerospace Corp.[g]	161	72	94	75
Orbital Sciences Corp.	56	19	57	73
Dynacs Engineering Co.	(a)	(a)	37	64
Ball Aerospace & Tech. Corp.	47	52	69	63
Sverdrup Technology Inc.................	27	27	29	58
Hamilton Sundstrand Space Systems[h]	(a)	9	55	58
Johnson Engineering Corp.	28	36	54	58
Swales & Associates Inc.	33	68	38	57
OAO Corp.	(a)	(a)	(a)	55
Raytheon Technical Services Co.[i] ...	44	43	45	49
Cortez III Service Corp...................	46	44	41	48
ITT Corp.......................................	25	35	57	47
Johnson Controls World Serv. Inc. ...	69	62	63	46

Source: National Aeronautics and Space Administration, "Annual Procurement Report" (Annually).
  a Not in list of major contractors for indicated year(s).
  b Includes awards previously reported separately as Lockheed Space Operations Co and Rockwell Space Operations Inc.
  c Includes awards previously reported separately as General Electric Co., Martin Marietta Corp., and Lockheed Missiles & Space Co.
  d Previously reported as Rockwell International Corp.
  f Previously reported as Hughes STX Corp.
  g Includes awards previously reported as Loral Aerospace Corp.
  h Previously reported as Hamilton Standard Space Systems.
  i Previously reported as Hughes Training Inc.

Aeronautics: the science that treats of the operation of aircraft, also, the art or science of operating aircraft.

Aerospace Employment: annual average calculated as one-twelfth of sum of monthly estimates of total number of persons employed during a designated pay period by the aircraft, missile, and space industries (SICs 372 and 376) plus estimated aerospace-related employment in the communications equipment (SIC 3662), instruments (SICs 381 and 382), and in certain other industries (SICs 28, 35, 73, 89, etc.)

Aerospace Industry: the industry engaged in research, development, and manufacture of aerospace systems including: manned and unmanned aircraft; missiles; spacecraft; space launch vehicles; propulsion, guidance, and control units for all of the foregoing; and a variety of airborne and ground-based equipment essential to the test, operation, and maintenance of flight vehicles.

Aerospace Payroll: estimated on the basis of average weekly *earnings* for a given calendar year for *production workers* plus an estimated annual salary for other employees.

Aerospace Sales: the *AIA* estimate of aerospace industry sales, developed by summing: *DoD* expenditures for aircraft, missiles, and space-related *procurement* and *RDT&E*; *NASA* expenditures for *research and development* and space flight control and data communications; *outlays* for space activities by other U.S. government departments and agencies; commercial sales of space-related products; net domestic and export sales of civil aircraft, engines, and parts; *Foreign Military Sales* and commercial exports of military aircraft, missiles, propulsion, and related parts; sales of *related products and*

services including: electronics, software, and ground support equipment; and sales of *non-aerospace products* which are produced in aerospace-manufacturing *establishments* and which use technology, processes, and materials derived from the *aerospace industry*.

AIA: Aerospace Industries Association of America, Inc., formerly Aircraft Industries Association.

Air Carriers: the commercial system of air transportation, consisting of domestic and international scheduled and charter service.

Aircraft: all airborne vehicles supported either by buoyancy or by dynamic action. Used in this volume in a restricted sense to mean an airplane—any winged aircraft including helicopters, but excluding gliders and guided missiles.

Aircraft Agreement (Agreement on Trade in Civil Aircraft): negotiated the Tokyo Round of the *Multilateral Trade Negotiations* and implemented January 1, 1980, providing for elimination of tariff and non-tariff trade barriers in the civil aircraft sector.

Aircraft Industry: the industry primarily engaged in the manufacture of aircraft, aircraft engines, and parts including propellers and auxiliary equipment. A sector of the *Aerospace Industry*.

Airframe: the structural components of an airplane, such as: fuselage, empennage, wings, landing gear, and engine mounts, but excluding such items as: engines, accessories, electronics, and other parts that may be replaced from time to time.

Airlines: see *Air Carriers*.

Appropriation (Federal Budget): an act of Congress authorizing an agency to incur *obligations* and make payments out of funds held by the Department of the Treasury.

Assets, Net: the sum of all recorded assets after reducing such amount by allowance of reserve for bad debts, *depreciation,* and amortization, but before deducting any liabilities, mortgages, or other indebtedness.

Astronautics: the art and science of designing, building, and operating manned or unmanned space objects.

Average Weekly Hours: average hours for which pay was received; different from standard or scheduled hours.

Avionics: communications, navigation, flight controls, and displays.

Backlog: the sales value of orders accepted (supported by legal documents) that have not yet passed through the sales account.

BMDO: Ballistic Missile Defense Organization, an agency of the Department of Defense.

Budget Authority: authority provided by the Congress; mainly in the form of *Appropriations,* which allows Federal agencies to incur *obligations* to spend or lend money.

Bureau of Economic Analysis (BEA): an agency of the Department of Commerce.

Bureau of Labor Statistics (BLS): an agency of the Department of Labor.

Bureau of the Census: an agency of the Department of Commerce.

Constant Dollars: calculated by dividing current ("then-year") dollars by appropriate price *deflator* and multiplying the result by 100.

Deflator: index used to convert a price level to one comparable with the price level at a different time, offsetting the effect of inflation. The base period, which equals 100, is usually specified as either a given fiscal or calendar year.

Depreciation: the general conversion of the depreciable cost of a fixed asset into expense, spread over its remaining life. There are a number of methods, all based on a periodic charge to an expense account and a corresponding credit to a reserve account.

Development: the process or activity of working out a basic design, idea, or piece of equipment. See also *Research and Development.*

DoD: Department of Defense.

DoE: Department of Energy.

DoT: Department of Transportation.

Durable Goods Industry: comprised of major manufacturing industry groups with SIC Codes 24, 25, and 32–39. All major manufacturing industry groups in SIC Codes 20–23 and 26–31 are considered nondurable goods manufacturing industry groups.

Earnings: the actual return to the worker for a stated period of time. Irregular bonuses, retroactive items, payments of various welfare benefits, and payroll taxes paid by employers are excluded.

Average Hourly Earnings: on a "gross" basis, reflecting not only changes in basic hourly and incentive wage rates, but also such variable factors as: premium pay for overtime, late shift work, and changes in output of workers paid for an incentive plan.

Average Weekly Earnings: derived by multiplying *average weekly hours* by *average hourly earnings.*

Establishment: the basis for reporting to the Census of Manufacturers; an operating facility in a single location.

Evaluation (Department of Defense): determination of technical suitability of material, equipment, or a system. See *RDT&E.*

Expenditures (Federal Budget): see *Outlays.*

Export-Import Bank of the United States (Eximbank): created in 1934 and established as an independent U.S. government agency in 1945, Eximbank is designed ". . . to aid in financing and to facilitate *exports* . . ." Eximbank receives no *appropriations* from the U.S. Congress. It is directed by statute to: (1) offer financing that is competitive with that offered exporters of other countries by their official export credit institutions, (2) determine that the transactions supported provide for a reasonable assurance of repayment, (3) supplement, but not compete with private sources of export financing, and (4) take into account the effect of its activities on small business, the domestic economy, and U.S. employment.

Exports: domestic merchandise including commodities which are grown, produced, or manufactured in the United States and commodities of foreign origin which have been changed in the United States from the form in which they were imported or which have been enhanced in value by further manufacture in the United States and which are traded or sold to other nations.

FAA: Federal Aviation Administration (formerly the Federal Aviation Agency), an agency of the Department of Transportation.

Facility: a physical plant or installation including: real property, building, structures, improvements, and plant equipment.

Fiscal Year (Federal Budget): beginning October 1, 1976, the fiscal years run from October 1 through September 30 and are designated by the year in which they end.

Flyaway Value: includes the cost of the airframe, engines, electronics, communications, armament, and other installed equipment.

Foreign Military Sales (FMS): export sales to foreign governments arranged through the Department of Defense, whereby DoD recovers full purchase price and administrative costs; often mistakenly used to include foreign military aid and foreign commercial sales as well.

FY: see *Fiscal Year.*

GDP (Gross Domestic Product): the market value of goods and services produced by labor and property located in the United States.

General Agreement on Tariffs and Trade (GATT): A multilateral treaty among more than 100 governments whose primary mission is the reduction of trade barriers. The World Trade Organization was established January 1, 1995 to implement the agreement and provide a forum to discuss trade issues.

General Aviation: all civil flying except that of *air carriers.*

Helicopter: a rotary-wing *aircraft* which depends principally for its support and motion in the air upon the lift generated by one or more power-driven rotors, rotating on substantially vertical axes. A helicopter is a *V/STOL.*

Heliport: an area, either at ground level or elevated on a structure, that is used for the landing and take-off of helicopters and includes some or all of the various facilities useful to helicopter operations such as: helicopter parking, hangar, waiting room, fueling, and maintenance equipment.

Helistop: a minimum facility *heliport,* either at ground level or elevated on a structure for the landing and takeoff of helicopters, but without such auxiliary facilities as: waiting room, hangar parking, etc.

ICBM: InterContinental Ballistic Missile, with a range of more than 5,000 miles.

Imports: classified as "general imports" or "imports for consumption." This volume refers generally to "imports for consumption," which are entries for immediate consumption plus merchandise withdrawn from bonded storage warehouses for consumption. Data are compiled from Import Entries filed with U.S. Customs officials and are in general based on the market value or price in the foreign country at the time of exportation of such merchandise, including the cost of containers and coverings, as well as other charges and expenses incidental to placing the merchandise in condition, packed and ready for shipment to the United States, but excluding import duties, insurance, freight, and other charges incidental to arrival of the goods in the United States. The foreign values of imported merchandise are converted into U.S. currency at the rate of exchange prevailing on the day the merchandise is shipped to the United States.

Income:

Net Operating Income: total *sales* less total operating costs.

Other Income and Expenses: includes interest income, royalty income, capital gains and losses, interest expense, cash discounts, etc.

Net Income (Before Income Taxes): *Net Operating Income* plus or minus *Other Income and Expenses.*

Net Income (After Income Taxes): *Net Income (Before Income Taxes)* less federal income taxes.

Lump-Sum Wage Payment: a one-time payment given in lieu of general wage increases and/or cost of living adjustments in labor settlements.

Manufacturing Industries: those *establishments* engaged in the mechanical or chemical transformation of inorganic or organic substances into new products, and usually described as plants, factories, or mills, which characteristically use power-driven machines and materials-handling equipment; also *establishments* engaged in assembling component parts of manufactured products if the new product is neither a structure nor other fixed improvement.

Merchandise Trade Balance: the difference between the value of U.S. goods exported to other countries and foreign goods imported into this country. The trade balance is generally regarded as "favorable" when *exports* exceed *imports*—a trade surplus—and "unfavorable" when *imports* exceed *exports*—a trade deficit.

Missile: sometimes applied to space launch vehicles, but more properly connotes automated weapons of warfare, that is, a weapon which has an integral system of guidance, as opposed to the unguided rocket.

Multilateral Trade Negotiations (MTN): a forum within the *GATT* in which countries negotiate to overcome their trade problems. Awaiting ratification by each of the 112 nations involved in the MTN, the "Uruguay Round" seeks to strengthen the *GATT* and expand its disciplines to new areas such as: services, agriculture, and trade-related intellectual property rights.

NASA: National Aeronautics and Space Administration.

NATO: North Atlantic Treaty Organization.

New Obligational Authority (Federal Budget): see *Budget Authority.*

Non-Aerospace Products and Services: products and services other than aircraft, missiles, space vehicles, and related propulsion and parts, produced or performed by *establishments* whose principal business is the development and/or manufacture of aerospace products.

OASD: Office of the Assistant Secretary of Defense.

Obligations (Federal Budget): commitments made by Federal agencies to pay out money for products, services, or other purposes—as distinct from the actual payments. Obligations incurred may not be larger than *budget authority.*

Orders, Net New: the sales value of new orders (supported by legal documents) minus cancellations during the period.

Other Aerospace Products and Services: all conversions, modifications, site activation, other aerospace products (including drones), services, plus *research and development* under contract, defined as: basic and applied research in the sciences and in engineering and design and development of prototype products and processes.

Other Customers: all customers other than the U.S. government to include but not limited to: *air carriers,* private citizens and corporations, and state, local, and foreign governments.

Outlays: checks issued, interest accrued on the public debt, or other payments made, net of refunds and reimbursements.

Overtime Hours: that portion of the gross *average weekly hours* which was in excess of regular hours and for which premium payments were made.

Passenger-Mile: one passenger moved one mile.

Payroll, All Manufacturing: includes the gross *earnings* paid in the calendar year to all employees on the payroll of operating manufacturing *establishments.* Includes all forms of compensation paid directly to workers such as: salaries, wages, commissions, dismissal pay, all bonuses, vacation and sick leave pay, and compensation in kind; prior to such deductions as: employees' Social Security contributions, withholding taxes, group insurance, union dues, and savings bonds. Does not include employers' Social Security contributions or other non-payroll labor costs such as: employees' pension plans, group insurance premiums, and workmen's compensation.

Procurement: the process whereby the executive agencies of the Federal Government acquire goods and services from enterprises other than the Federal Government.

Production Workers: includes working foremen and all non-supervisory workers (including lead-men and trainees) engaged in fabricating, processing, assembling, inspection, receiving, storage, handling, janitorial services, product development, auxiliary production for plant's own use, and recordkeeping and services closely associated with the above production operations.

RDT&E (Department of Defense): Research, Development, Test, and Evaluation.

Related Products and Services: sales of electronics, software, and ground equipment in support of aerospace products, plus sales by aerospace manufacturing *establishments* of systems and equipment which are generally derived from the industry's aerospace technological expertise in design, materials, and processes, but which are intended for applications other than flight.

Research: see *Research and Development.*

Research and Development:

Research: systematic study directed toward fuller scientific knowledge or understanding of the subject studied. Research is classified as either basic or applied according to the objectives of the sponsoring agency.

Applied Research: with the objective of gaining knowledge or understanding necessary for determining the means by which a recognized and specific need may be met.

Basic Research: with the objective of gaining fuller knowledge or understanding of the fundamental aspects of phenomena and of observable facts without specific applications toward processes or products in mind.

Development: the systematic use of scientific knowledge directed toward the production of useful materials, devices, systems, or methods including design and development of prototypes and processes.

Independent Research and Development (IR&D): a term devised by the Department of Defense and used by Federal agencies to differentiate between a contractor's research and development technical effort performed under a contract, grant, or other arrangement (R&D) and that which is self-initiated and self-funded (IR&D).

Industrial Research and Development: research and development work performed within company facilities, funded by company or Federal funds, and excluding company-financed research and development

contracted to outside organizations such as: research institutions, universities and colleges, or other non-profit organizations.

Rotorcraft: an *aircraft* which, in all its usual flight attitudes, is supported in the air wholly or in part by a rotor or rotors (i.e., airfoils rotating or revolving about an axis). See *Helicopter.*

Sales: net of returns, allowances, and discounts, the dollar value of shipments, including dealer's commissions, if any, which have passed through the sales account.

Satellite: a body that revolves around a larger body, such as the Moon revolving around the Earth, or a man-made object revolving about any body such as the Sun, Earth, or Moon.

SIC (Standard Industrial Classification): a system developed by the U.S. government to define the industrial composition of the economy, facilitating comparability of statistics. See *Aerospace Industry* for explanation of SIC codes applicable to the aerospace industry.

Space Vehicle: an artificial body operating in outer space (beyond the Earth's atmosphere).

Stockholder's Equity: *assets* minus all obligations of the corporation, except those to stockholders. Annual data are average equity for the year (using four end-of-quarter figures). For details, see "Quarterly Financial Report for Manufacturing, Mining and Trade Corporations," compiled by the *Bureau of the Census.*

STOL: short take-off and landing *aircraft.*

Test (Department of Defense): an experiment designed to assess progress in attainment or accomplishment of *development* objectives (see *RDT&E*).

Thrust: the driving force exerted by an engine, particularly an aircraft or missile engine, in propelling the vehicle to which it is attached.

Ton-Mile: one ton moved one mile.

Total Obligational Authority: the sum of *budget authority* granted or requested from the Congress in a given year, plus unused *budget authority* from prior years.

Trade Balance: see *Merchandise Trade Balance.*

Transition Quarter (Tr. Qtr.): the three-month interval from July 1, 1976 to September 30, 1976 belonging to neither Fiscal Year 1976 nor Fiscal Year 1977. See *Fiscal Year.*

Turbine, Turbo: a mechanical device or engine that spins in reaction to a fluid flow that passes through or over it. Frequently used in "turboprop" or "turbojet."

UK: United Kingdom.

US: United States of America.

USA: United States Army, an agency of the U.S. Department of Defense.

USAF: United States Air Force, an agency of the U.S. Department of Defense.

USN: United States Navy, an agency of the U.S. Department of Defense.

USSR: Union of Soviet Socialist Republics. Statistics continue to exclude this region until official data from the now independent republics become available.

Utility Aircraft: an aircraft designed for general purpose flying.

V/STOL: vertical short take-off and/or landing *aircraft.*

INDEX